VOICES
SESSION GUIDES

Voices
Session Guides

Board of Publications
of the Christian Reformed Church

Acknowledgments

The Education Department is grateful to Mr. Dan Vander Ark for many ideas which are incorporated into this workbook. Mr. Vander Ark is a veteran high school teacher and principal at Holland Christian High School, Holland, Michigan.

Session Guides was written, edited, and produced by the Education Department of the Christian Reformed Church. Any inquiries, suggestions, or criticisms related to *Session Guides* or other parts of the *Voices* course should be directed to Education Department, 2850 Kalamazoo SE, Grand Rapids, MI 49560.

Most of the Scripture quotations in this publication are from the Revised Standard Version of the Bible copyrighted 1946, 1952, 1971, 1973 by the Division of Christian Education of the National Council of Churches of Christ in the USA and used by permission.

Occasional use is made of the New International Version. HOLY BIBLE: New International Version. Copyright 1978 by the New York International Bible Society. Used by permission of the Zondervan Bible Publishers.

BIBLE WAY ♱ VOICES, Second Edition ©1983, Board of Publications of the Christian Reformed Church, 2850 Kalamazoo SE, Grand Rapids, MI 49560. All rights reserved. Printed in the United States of America.

ISBN 0-933140-90-8

Contents

Preface

Please use this workbook with *Promises* by Dr. Nederhood (radio/TV minister with the Back to God Hour) and as a guide to class discussion and Bible study. Bring it, along with *Promises*, to each class session.

Generally you'll be asked to read a chapter in *Promises* at home; your instructor may also ask you to complete all or part of section A of this workbook at home. Then, in class, you'll typically use the session guides to discuss *Promises* (section A), to direct your Bible study (section B), and to close the class session in worship (section C).

Use *Session Guides* as your notebook for the course. Write in it and save it as your personal record of what you've learned about God's Word.

Session Guides is a *workbook*—that should be honestly admitted. It takes a certain amount of work to study God's Word, though that work needn't be dull or tedious. Studying God's Word—together—can and should be one of the greatest and most enjoyable things we do. More important, though, than our work or our enjoyment is our response to the Scriptures. God's Word is first of all a Word to be believed.

We hope that this workbook will bring you into God's Word and that his Word and Spirit will make you strong in him.

The Education Department Staff

Agenda for
Introductory Session

I. Getting Acquainted

Please take a minute to tell something about yourself (your name, school, job, special interests, and so on).

II. Introducing This Course

A. Materials and Methods

1. Bible

2. *Promises, Promises, Promises* by Joel Nederhood

3. *Session Guides* Workbook

B. Goals

Listed below are some of the goals of this course. Please put a *1* by the goal you think most important, a *2* by the next most important, and so on. There's a space to add goals of your own, if you wish. Doing this exercise will help your teacher do a better job of presenting the material to meet your needs.

THIS COURSE SHOULD TEACH ME TO

A. __3__ develop the habit of daily Bible reading.

B. __4__ know what my church teaches about the Bible.

C. __2__ personally regard the Bible as God's Word and respond to that Word in obedience and worship.

D. __1__ read the Bible with more understanding, knowing how to interpret it and how to relate a passage to the rest of the Bible.

E. __6__ see the Bible as one book telling the developing story of God's relationship with his people.

F. __5__ know major events and persons in the history of God's dealing with his people.

G. _____

H. _____

III. Closing the Session

Suppose you had to pick one passage from Scripture to convince an unbeliever that you believe the Bible is a special book, a book from God, a book of hope and salvation. What passage would you pick and why? For our closing devotions please be ready to read your passage to the class.

For Next Time: Please read chapter 1 of *Promises* and complete section *A* of the session guide for that chapter, as your instructor directs. Notice that each chapter of *Promises* includes daily Bible readings for home devotions.

Session Guide 1

Promises, Promises, Promises

A. Chapter Review

1. Personal comments/questions on chapter 1:

2. In what ways is the Bible a single book?

3. How is the Bible a covenant book?

It tells us of God's promises to his people and also proves God will keep his covenant.

4. Dr. Nederhood compares God's covenant to a marriage covenant. How are they alike? How different?

they are both promises

a marriage promise might be broken, but God will never break his promise.

covenant - partnership God has 11 with his people to carry out his purposes

B. Bible Study

Although the entire Bible is the record of God's covenantal relationship with humanity, some chapters speak very directly of the covenantal relationship. Psalm 25 is one of those chapters. Read it through, then discuss the questions which follow:

1. Find the two verses in the psalm which mention the word *covenant*. What is God doing with the covenant? What are God's people doing?

    verses= 10, 14

2. Under the two headings below, list by verse the *specific* covenantal activities of God and his people, as represented by David. One example is given.

GOD (making known his covenant)	GOD'S PEOPLE (keeping the covenant)
—protects his people (vv. 1–3) saves; teaches; leads (vv. 4,5) loves; forgiveness blesses; delivers	—trust in God (v. 1) wait patiently faithful fear pray praise

3. What can we learn from the above comparison about the partnership between God and humanity? *imbalanced*

God does work; we accept

we are expected to wait, trust, pray, & obey.

4. How can studying the Bible, as we'll be doing in this course, help us keep our covenantal obligations to God? (See vv. 4, 8–9, 14.)

teaches us

learn more about him.

C. Worship

We often break our commitments, but God doesn't. He is faithful to his promises; Psalm 25 speaks more than once of God's "steadfast love." But no psalm mentions God's steadfast love more than Psalm 136! In its original use, it's likely that a leader first sang a sentence about a mighty act of God in Israel's history; then all the people joined in the refrain, praising God for his steadfast love.

For closing devotions today, try this approach with Psalm 136:1–9, 23–26. One person should read the opening half of each verse, with the rest of the class reading the refrain.

For Next Time: Read chapter 2 in *Promises,* "The Greatest Fact." Complete section A of the session guide for chapter 2, as your teacher directs. See the end of chapter 2 for suggested Bible readings this week at home.

The Greatest Fact

A. Chapter Review

1. Personal comments/questions on chapter 2:

2. What is the "most important fact" revealed in Genesis 1, 2, and 3? List three or four positive implications of this fact—things that encourage us as Christians living in God's world.

3. How does the author feel when he thinks about being a *fallen* image-bearer of God? Can you understand his feelings? What does Dr. Nederhood say is his dominant impression of the fall?

4. We sometimes think of redemption in personal terms: God saves *me*. That's true, of course, but what's a more complete way of talking about God's redemption?

B. Bible Study

Since one of the goals of this course is to improve our Bible-reading skills, we'll be learning half a dozen important questions which can help us interpret *any* Bible passage. The first "How to Study the Bible" question, which we'll learn and apply today, is very important:

WHAT DOES THIS PASSAGE SAY ABOUT THE COVENANT
(PARTNERSHIP) BETWEEN GOD AND HIS PEOPLE?

When we ask this question about a passage, we are looking for two things: first, evidence of the partnership between God and his people; and second, evidence that points toward Jesus Christ, the fulfillment of the covenant.

Today's Bible study applies the covenant question to Genesis 3:1–21. Read the passage, then tell what the following verses have to do with God's covenant with his people. If possible, write down the number of a verse or verses in each passage that especially show the covenant relationship.

1. Genesis 3:1–7

2. Genesis 3:8–1?

3. Genesis 3:14–21

C. Worship

A transcript of the tape, segment 1, follows:

Adam in the Garden

Adam in the suburban garden
Among the television trees,
Tasting the fruit of the Tree of Knowledge,
Carelessly tosses the core over his shoulder.

It explodes, brilliant as a million acetylene torches,
Deafening as a million sonic booms.
It shatters the picture windows and knocks
The cross of First Church out of the sky.

The sun hides his face behind a mushroom cloud.
The clock on the Federal Building and Loan Office
No longer reports the interest rate
Or flashes the time and temperature.

The net alert station is silent,
The news fails to report the flash,
Church bells are silent. Sermons on
Unilateral disarmament have been cancelled.

God, abandoned, lonely, obscured by smoke,
Stubs His toe on a steeple
Buried in the ashes of the garden and
Calls, "Adam, where are you?"

by Elmer F. Suderman. International copyright held
by *Ball State University Forum*. Used by permission.

For Next Time: Chapter 3 in *Promises*, "The Beginning of Now"—read how the early chapters in Genesis tell about the beginning of our own times. As usual, complete section A, as your instructor specifies.

Session Guide 3

The Beginning of Now

A. Chapter Review

1. Personal comments/questions on chapter 3:

2. The author comments that in Genesis 4–11 we find "the beginning of now." What does this mean?

3. The flood is not a cute story for little kids, says Dr. Nederhood. What does he say it teaches us about God?

B. Bible Study

1. Read Genesis 6:5-13, 17-19. Why did God destroy *all* life on the planet, not just human life? And why did he save Noah?

2. After the flood, God came back to man and established the covenant again. Like most covenants, this one had three basic parts:
   a. partners (participants):

   b. obligations (promises made by both parties):

   c. sign (a symbol to remind each party of the obligations):

   Read Genesis 8:20-22 and 9:7-17 to find the three parts. Write them down in the space above.

C. Worship

Read in unison Genesis 8:22 and Isaiah 54:10, as follows:

While the earth remains, seedtime and harvest, cold and heat, summer and winter, day and night, shall not cease.

For the mountains may depart and the hills be removed, but my steadfast love shall not depart from you, and my covenant of peace shall not be removed, says the Lord, who has compassion on you.

Think about these comments from Rev. Andrew Kuyvenhoven:

Reflecting on the covenant with creation,...we must never again take for granted that the earth continues to exist, that the sun comes up in the morning, and that a measure of order and happiness can be found in our world. Those are signs of the universal kindness to which God pledged himself in the covenant with Noah. Instead of complaining about the adversities and taking good things in stride,...we must be aware that good things in the present world come to us in spite of sin...and thanks to God's covenant faithfulness. We are living under threatening clouds, but they are tinted with the rainbow of God's mercy.

Think about one part of life on this planet which you tend to take for granted, but which comes from the gracious hand of God. In a silent prayer, thank God for this gift—and all his gifts—to our world.

For Next Time: Chapter 4 of *Promises* claims Abraham—that ancient father of all believers—was really a modern man, in more ways than one. Read chapter 4 and find out how. Complete section *A* of the session guide, as your instructor suggests.

Sands of the Seashore People

A. Chapter Review

1. Personal comments/questions on chapter 4:

2. True/false quiz on the chapter

   a. _____ Before God called him, Abraham was a poor nomad.

   b. _____ Abraham lived about 2000 years before Christ.

   c. _____ Before God called him, Abraham probably worshiped false gods.

   d. _____ A covenant in Abraham's day implied equal partners who exchanged promises which were guaranteed by a sacrifice or some other sign.

   e. _____ The author suggests that God's promises must have seemed unreasonable to Abraham.

   f. _____ Because of his doubt, Abraham is not listed among the great heroes of faith.

   g. _____ God's promises to us, says the author, may seem unreasonable.

   h. _____ We earn our righteousness before God by being his obedient servants and by having great faith in him.

   i. _____ The author agrees that our baptism is a sign of our faith.

   j. _____ If we believe in Christ, we are Abraham's children, "sands of the seashore people."

Note: The chart on the following pages shows how God's covenant of grace runs through the Bible. Your instructor will explain the chart in class today, but it will take on more meaning as you study the Bible together during the next few weeks and months. Please refer to the chart often during that study.

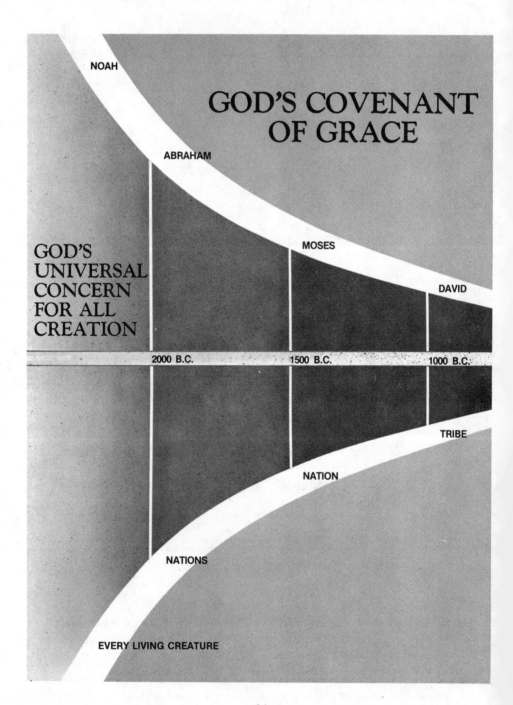

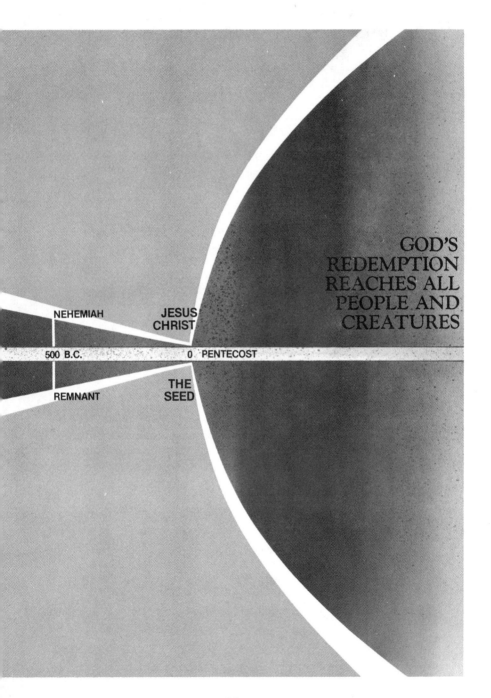

NEHEMIAH

JESUS CHRIST

GOD'S
REDEMPTION
REACHES ALL
PEOPLE AND
CREATURES

500 B.C.　　　　　　　0　PENTECOST

REMNANT

THE
SEED

B. Bible Study

Read Genesis 17, then discuss the partners, promises, and sign of the covenant of grace, using the questions below to guide your discussion.

Partners (participants)
1. God and Abraham are the partners, of course (vv. 1–2), but to whom is the covenant extended in verse 7?

2. What New Testament verse links all believers to Abraham?

3. Find proof in verses 1–3 of chapter 17 that God is the *dominant* partner.

4. Does this chapter give any reasons why God chose Abraham to be his covenant partner? Was there something special, unique about Abraham?

Promises (obligations)
5. What did God promise to Abraham and his descendants (vv. 2, 4, 6–8)?

6. Abraham's obligation was "to keep the covenant" (v. 9). Find some specific examples from chapter 17 which show what this meant.

7. Abraham and Sarah are recorded as laughing at God's promises. Can you understand that reaction? Comment.

Sign
8. What was the Old Testament sign of the covenant? What was the penalty for not observing the sign?

9. How does the Old Testament sign of the covenant provide a good argument for New Testament baptism of infants?

C. Worship

To believe God's promises takes great faith. Abraham, though far from perfect, had that kind of faith. How many of us wouldn't laugh if, when we were one hundred years old, God told us we would have a child, and that our descendants would be as numerous as the sands on the beach? How many of us would then be obedient enough to give up that only son at God's request?

God still comes with promises that sound unreal. To believe them takes all the faith we have. What *for you* takes this kind of faith? Write a couple of endings to this sentence:

By faith I believe that...

Share your statements with others, if you wish.

For Next Time: Exodus, Numbers, Leviticus, Deuteronomy. Dull books, right? Dr. Nederhood understands those feelings, but in chapter 5 of *Promises* he explains what these books can teach us about God. Read chapter 5 and complete section A of the session guide for next time, please.

The Religion of Moses

A. Chapter Review

1. Personal questions/comments on chapter 5:

2. What is your personal reaction to reading the Pentateuch? Will any of Dr. Nederhood's comments help you in your future reading of these books? Comment.

3. Today's session focuses on the Law of God. Summarize what Dr. Nederhood says about God's Law.

B. Bible Study

Problem: Why does the Bible include two apparently identical passages listing the Ten Commandments?
To solve the problem, we'll work on some detailed comparisons between the two "Law" passages. Your instructor will probably ask you to work on *one* of the seven comparisons below.

1. Read Exodus 19:5 and Deuteronomy 5:2–3. In what ways are these passages alike?

2. Read Exodus 20:2 and Deuteronomy 5:6. List three ways these passages are alike.

3. Read Exodus 20:3–17 and Deuteronomy 5:7–21. Are these passages entirely alike? Explain.

4. Read Exodus 20:18–20 and Deuteronomy 5:22–27. In what ways are these passages alike? Look especially at the role of Moses.

5. Read Exodus 19:1–2 and Deuteronomy 1:1–8. What important differences can you observe in the *people* to whom the Law is addressed? Look especially at time, place, and situation.

6. Read Exodus 19:16–25 and Deuteronomy 5:1–6. One of these passages is history—it tells events as they happened. The other is a sermon. Which is which? How do you know?

7. Read Exodus 19:6; 20:20 and Deuteronomy 6:4–9. What was the purpose of the Law of God for the audience in Exodus? For the audience in Deuteronomy?

After hearing how other students answered their assigned question, what conclusions can you draw about why the Bible includes two nearly identical passages on the Law?

31

Answer two "How to Study the Bible" questions on the passages we've just studied:

1. *What does this passage say about the covenant (partnership) between God and his people?*

2. Add a question on *audience*, based on today's lesson:

C. Worship

Read Psalm 19:7-10 as an expression of thanks to God for his law. Notice the words the psalmist substitutes for *law*: testimony, precepts, commandment, fear, ordinances.

For Next Time: Read chapter 6 in *Promises*. Joshua and Judges, says Dr. Nederhood, sound like how the West was won—the sounds, fights, and blood. Why read these books, then? Chapter 6 gives an answer.
   Complete section A of the next session guide, as required.

An Ugly Chapter

A. Chapter Review

1. Personal comments/questions on chapter 6:

2. The author says the books of Joshua and Judges show some "of the ugliest chapters in Israel's history." Give two examples of this.

3. What does Dr. Nederhood say these "ugly" chapters teach us about God's people? About God?

B. Bible Study

Read Judges 6:1–24.

1. How was Israel suffering? Why?

2. Why did Israel turn to the Lord (v. 6)? Do our prayers sometimes have the same motivation?

3. How had God kept his covenant promises (vv. 7–10)? How had Israel violated its covenant obligations?

4. How would you describe Gideon's faith (vv. 11–16)? In what ways are most of us like him in times of trouble?

5. A covenant includes a promise and a sign. What promise did Gideon receive? What was Gideon's obligation? What was the sign, and how did Gideon react to it?

6. This chapter reflects a cycle, or pattern, that occurs repeatedly in the books of Joshua and Judges. The cycle begins with Israel's disobedience. See if you can complete the rest of the cycle, below:

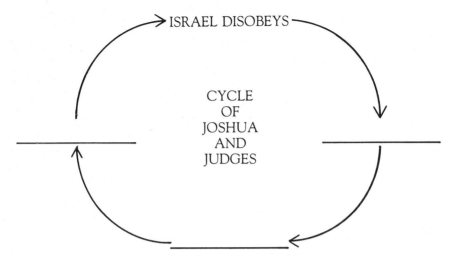

7. Look again at what Dr. Nederhood says we can learn from Joshua and Judges. Does your study of Judges 6 confirm this? Please comment.

C. Worship

Reflect silently on how our own lives often bog down in the vicious cycle Israel found herself in—sin, punishment, prayer for help, deliverance, sin, and so on. Praise God for his faithfulness by reading Psalm 103, 100, or 136 (or a similar passage of your choice).

For Next Time: Please read chapter 7—"The Hyphenated Israelite"—as well as the four chapters of the book of Ruth.

Session Guide 7

The Hyphenated Israelite

A. Bible Study and Chapter Review

1. So far we've practiced using two "How to Study the Bible" questions. Please write them below, from memory:

Our study of the book of Ruth introduces a third question:

WHO IS THE AUTHOR AND WHAT IS THE AUTHOR'S PURPOSE IN WRITING?

---

2. To determine author and purpose, a careful reading is necessary. Since you've already done that with the book of Ruth, we'll review the highlights with a dramatization on tape, taken from the NIV. Be sure to ask any questions you might have about plot or characters.

A transcript of the tape, segment 3, follows:

Narrator: In the days when the judges ruled, there was a famine in the land, and a man from Bethlehem in Judah, together with his wife and two sons, went to live for a while in the country of Moab. The man's name was Elimelech, his wife's name Naomi, and the names of his two sons were Mahlon and Kilion. They were Ephrathites from Bethlehem, Judah. And they went to Moab and lived there.

    Now Elimelech, Naomi's husband, died, and she was left with her two sons. They married Moabite women, one named Orpah and the other Ruth. After they had lived there about ten years, both Mahlon and Kilion also died, and Naomi was left without her two sons and her husband.

    When she heard in Moab that the Lord had come to the aid of his people by providing food for them, Naomi and her daughters-in-law prepared to return home from there. With her two daughters-in-law she left the place where she had been living and set out on the road that would take them back to the land of Judah.

    Then Naomi said to her two daughters-in-law,

Naomi: Go back, each of you, to your mother's home. May the Lord show kindness to you, as you have shown to your dead and to me. May the Lord grant that each of you will find rest in the home of another husband.

Narrator: Then she kissed them and they wept aloud and said to her,

Ruth: We will go back with you to your people.

Naomi: Return home, my daughters. Why would you come with me?
...Am I going to have any more sons, who could become your husbands? Return home, my daughters; I am too old to have another husband. Even if I thought there was still hope for me—even if I had a husband tonight and then gave birth to sons—would you wait until they grew up? Would you remain un-married for them? No, my daughters. It is more bitter for me than for you, because the Lord's hand has gone out against me!

Narrator: At this they wept again. Then Orpah kissed her mother-in-law good-by, but Ruth clung to her.

Naomi: Look, your sister-in-law is going back to her people and her gods. Go back with her.

Ruth: Don't urge me to leave you or to turn back from you. Where you go I will go, and where you stay I will stay. Your people will be my people and your God my God. Where you die I will die, and there I will be buried. May the Lord deal with me, be it ever so severely, if anything but death separates you and me.

Narrator: When Naomi realized that Ruth was determined to go with her, she stopped urging her.
So the two women went on until they came to Bethlehem. When they arrived in Bethlehem, the whole town was stirred because of them, and the women exclaimed,

Women: Can this be Naomi?

Naomi: Don't call me Naomi. Call me Mara, because the Almighty has made my life very bitter. I went away full, but the Lord has brought me back empty. Why call me Naomi? The Lord has af-flicted me; the Almighty has brought misfortune upon me.

Narrator: So Naomi returned from Moab accompanied by Ruth the Moabitess, her daughter-in-law, arriving in Bethlehem as the barley harvest was beginning.

Now Naomi had a relative on her husband's side, from the clan of Elimelech, a man of standing, whose name was Boaz.
And Ruth the Moabitess said to Naomi,

Ruth: Let me go to the fields and pick up the leftover grain behind anyone in whose eyes I find favor.

Naomi: Go ahead, my daughter.

Narrator: So she went out and began to glean in the fields behind the harvesters. As it turned out, she found herself working in a field belonging to Boaz. . . . So Ruth stayed close to the servant girls of Boaz to glean until the barley and wheat harvests were finished. And she lived with her mother-in-law.
One day Naomi her mother-in-law said to her:

Naomi: My daughter, should I not try to find a home for you, where you will be well provided for? Is not Boaz, with whose servant girls you have been, a kinsman of ours? Tonight he will be winnowing barley on the threshing floor. Wash and perfume yourself, and put on your best clothes. Then go down to the threshing floor, but don't let him know you are there until he has finished eating and drinking. When he lies down, note the place where he is lying. Then go and uncover his feet and lie down. He will tell you what to do.

Ruth: I will do whatever you say.

Narrator: So she went down to the threshing floor and did everything her mother-in-law told her to do.
When Boaz had finished eating and drinking and was in good spirits, he went over to lie down at the far end of the grain pile. Ruth approached quietly, uncovered his feet and lay down. In the middle of the night something startled the man, and he turned and discovered a woman lying at his feet.

Boaz: Who are you?

Ruth: I am your servant Ruth. Spread the corner of your garment over me, since you are a kinsman-redeemer.

Boaz: The Lord bless you, my daughter. This kindness is greater than that which you showed earlier. You have not run after the younger men, whether rich or poor. And now, my daughter, don't be afraid. I will do for you all you ask. All my fellow townsmen know that you are a woman of noble character. Although it is true that I am near of kin, there is a kinsman-redeemer nearer than I. Stay here for the night, and in the morning if he wants to redeem, good; let him redeem. But if he is not willing, I vow that, as surely as the Lord livès, I will do it. Lie here until morning.

Narrator: So she lay at his feet until morning, but got up before anyone could be recognized.

Boaz: Don't let it be known that a woman came to the threshing floor. Bring me the shawl you are wearing and hold it out.

Narrator: When she did so, he poured into it six measure of barley and put it on her. Then he went back to town. When Ruth came to her mother-in-law, Naomi asked,

Naomi: How did it go, my daughter?

Narrator: Then Ruth told her everything Boaz had done for her.

Naomi: Wait, my daughter, until you find out what happens. For the man will not rest until the matter is settled.

Narrator: Meanwhile Boaz went up to the town gate and sat there. When the kinsman-redeemer he had mentioned came along, Boaz successfully claimed the right to act as next of kin. Then Boaz announced to the elders and all the people:

Boaz: Today you are witnesses that I have bought from Naomi all the property of Elimelech, Kilion and Mahlon. I have also acquired Ruth the Moabitess, Mahlon's widow, as my wife, in order to maintain the name of the dead with his property, so that his name will not disappear from among his family or from the town records. Today you are witnesses!

Elders: We are witnesses. May the Lord make the woman who is coming into your home like Rachel and Leah, who together built up the house of Israel. May you have standing in Ephratah and be famous in Bethlehem. Through the offspring the Lord gives you by this young woman, may your family be like that of Perez, whom Tamar bore to Judah.

Narrator: So Boaz took Ruth and she became his wife. And the Lord enabled her to conceive, and she gave birth to a son. The women said to Naomi:

Women: Praise be to the Lord, who this day has not left you without a kinsman-redeemer. May he become famous throughout Israel! He will renew your life and sustain you in your old age. For your daughter-in-law, who loves you and who is better to you than seven sons, has given him birth.

Narrator: Then Naomi took the child, laid him in her lap, and cared for him. The women living there said, "Naomi has a son." And they named him Obed. He was the father of Jesse, the father of David.

3. Work in small groups to decide which of the following statements most accurately reflects the author's purpose for the book of Ruth. In other words, which statement best explains why Ruth is included in God's Word? Be ready to defend your choice by referring to the book itself.

_____ A. I think whoever wrote Ruth did so to inspire us. The author is saying to readers of all times and places: "Be like Ruth. Be loyal as Ruth was. Trust God as Ruth did. And God will reward you, as he rewarded Ruth." That's why this book is in the Bible, I'm sure.

_____ B. The book of Ruth is an inspiring story and we can all learn from Ruth. But Ruth was written to tell us mainly about God, not about people. This book teaches us that God takes care of those who trust him, no matter what their nationality. Ruth, a foreigner, said to Naomi, "Your God will be my God." To those who trust in God as Ruth did, all things will work out for the best. This book tells us we have a God who loves us and protects us. I think that's its main purpose.

_____ C. To me, the book of Ruth was written to show God interacting with his human partners to preserve his covenant and bring his people to salvation. God reaches out in power and love to use ordinary people like Ruth and Boaz to continue his covenant. I think the whole point of the book—and the reason it's in the Bible—is in chapter 4, when Ruth and Boaz have a son, Obed, who is the father of Jesse, the father of David. And from David's line comes Jesus Christ.

_____ D. Ruth was written as a Christian love story, to show how God can bring together two people of entirely different backgrounds. To me the author is saying, "If you have God in your marriage, that's all that really counts."

_____ E. I think it's wrong to limit an author's purpose, especially an author who's inspired by the unlimited Holy Spirit. Why can't God's Word say different things to different people? I think the book of Ruth could inspire one person to be like Ruth; another person could be comforted by its picture of a loving, almighty God; another could see it as a story of God's preserving the covenant; someone else might read it as a Christian love story. What's the difference? I think we've got to let our feelings speak to us—through the Holy Spirit, of course.

Notes:

4. Dr. Nederhood says Ruth and even 1 and 2 Samuel must be viewed in terms of David. Why? What was so important about David?

5. Dr. Nederhood comments that "it's sometimes hard for me to see how the establishment of David's kingdom directly affects me, a Christian living in the twentieth century." He notes, though, that Ruth and Samuel and Saul and David help God "take on flesh and blood here." What does he mean by this? How does this relate to *us*?

B. Worship

Someone once said that God's caring for his people is like a beautiful tapestry. God knows where every thread and knot fits to make his creation and creatures one beautiful unity. But from our human perspective, like Ruth and Naomi in their troubles, we sometimes see only the underside of the tapestry, the knots and dangling bits of thread.

Answer 26 of the Heidelberg Catechism reminds us of the way we ought to trust our almighty God:

I trust him so much that I do not doubt
  he will provide
    whatever I need
    for body and soul,
  and he will turn to my good
    whatever adversity he sends me
    in this sad world.

He is able to do this because he is almighty God;
he desires to do this because he is a faithful Father.

For Next Time: Dr. Nederhood says he "stays sane while reading" Kings and Chronicles by remembering four things. Look for these as you read chapter 8. Complete section A, as assigned by your instructor.

Session Guide 8
Staying Sane While Reading

A. Chapter Review

1. Personal comments/questions on chapter 8:

2. What is Tony's problem? Can you understand why he feels this way?

3. Dr. Nederhood keeps four things in mind while reading Kings and Chronicles. Either underline them in the chapter or list them below:

4. The author concludes that these books about Israel's decline help him "remember Jesus." What are his reasons?

B. Bible Study

Read 1 Kings 18:17–46; 19.

Today's Bible study will apply Dr. Nederhood's four guidelines given in chapter 8.

Guideline: Beware of the corruption and power of false religion.

1. What was the false religion? How widespread was it?

2. Give one example of its corrupting power.

3. What do you think was the author's purpose in these chapters?

Guideline: Remember that we live in a moral universe in which sin is eventually punished.

4. How had Israel broken the covenant?

5. How was Israel punished for her sin?

6. Why was Elijah depressed (19:1–8)?

Guideline: Remember that God is faithful to his people; his promises are always
  kept.

7. Make a list of all the signs of God's faithfulness to his covenant people, as
   shown in chapters 18 and 19.

8. In what ways had Elijah been an obedient covenant partner? How did he
   show he was still human and vulnerable?

Guideline: Remember the bright places of God's mercy, pointing to his fulfilled
  promise of a Redeemer.

9. What to you is most encouraging about the events in these chapters?

10. Do these chapters in any way help you to "remember Jesus"? Please com-
    ment.

C. Worship

"Be still, and know that I am God." Sometimes God comes to us in quiet, un-
dramatic ways, as he came to Elijah in a "still, small voice." When we look for

God in our lives, we too need to listen, to reflect, to be silent...or we may miss his voice.

A transcript of the tape, segment 4, follows:

the last Word

Be still and know...

But they walked and they ran,
And they marched and they rode,
And they flew and they drove,
And they bused and they commuted.

Be still and know that...

But they gathered and they met,
And they communed and they congregated,
And they assembled in circles,
And lined up in rows and they organized.

Be still and know that I...

But they conversed and they spoke,
And they shouted and they shook,
And they cried and they laughed,
And they murmured and complained.

Be still and know that I am...

But the marchers went forward,
The buses rolled on,
The circles went round,
The lines kept moving,
And the shouts and the cries,
And the laughter and the sighs,
And the murmurings and the complaints,
Grew louder and stronger
Whirling and swirling
Faster and faster
Until suddenly—it stopped.

And everybody fell off.

Be still and know that I am God.

By Sandra Duguid from *The Country of the Risen King* by Merle Meeter. Copyright 1978 by Baker Book House and used by permission.

For Next Time: Please read chapter 9—"The Psalm Problem"—and complete section A, as assigned by your instructor.

Session Guide 9
The Psalm Problem

A. Chapter Review

This time use chapter 9 as a take-off point for your own reactions to the Psalms. Please come to class ready to comment on these questions:

1. What do I think of the Psalms? Do I have any kind of a "psalm problem," such as that described by Dr. Nederhood?

2. Which psalms, if any, have been especially meaningful to me? (Perhaps you could pick one such psalm and tell why you especially appreciate it.)

3. Is there anything I can do to increase my appreciation of the Psalms?

B. Bible Study

Today's Bible study applies four "How to Study the Bible" questions (three familiar questions, one new one) to Psalm 22. The new question is this:

49

WHAT IS THE LITERARY STYLE OF THIS PASSAGE?

We'll work through the questions together. Please take notes, since next week you'll be asked to apply the four questions—on your own—to a different psalm.

1. *Who is the author and what is the author's purpose in writing?*
   Notes:

2. *To what audience is the original message addressed?*
   Notes:

3. What does this passage say about the covenant (partnership) between God and his people?
   Notes:

4. What is the literary style of this passage?
   Notes:

C. Worship

Psalm 22 is about the suffering of God's people...and God's deliverance. Joseph Bayly, in "A Psalm at Children's Hospital," shows that today's troubles also need psalms for expression.

A transcript of the tape, segment 5, follows:

A Psalm at Children's Hospital

I find it hard Lord
agonizing hard
to stand here
looking through the glass
at this my infant son.
What suffering
is in this world
to go through pain of birth
and then through
pain of knife
within the day.
What suffering
is in the world
this never ending
pain parade
from birth
to death.
He moves
a bit
not much
how could an infant
stuffed with tubes
cut sewed and bandaged
move more than that?
Some day he'll shout
and run a race
roll down a grassy hill
ice skate
on frosty nights like this.
He'll sing
and laugh
I know he will Lord.
But if not
if You should take him home
to Your home
help me then remember

how Your Son suffered
and you stood by
watching
agonizing watching
waiting
to bring all suffering to an end
forever
on a day
yet to be.
Look Lord
he sleeps.
I must go now.
Thank You for staying
nearer than oxygen
than dripping plasma
to my son.
Please be that near
to mother
sister brothers
and to me.

From *Psalms for My Life*, by Joseph Bayly.
Published by Tyndale House Publishers, Inc., © 1969. Used by permission.

For Next Time: Here is a special assignment, in addition to reading chapter 10 of *Promises.* Working with a psalm picked by you or your instructor, answer the four "How to Study the Bible" questions and be ready to share your answers with the class at our next meeting. Answers can be written in section *B* of next week's session guide. You'll also find a few comments there to help you with the assignment.

Session Guide 10

"A" Is for Adultery

A. Chapter Review

Note: Since chapter 10 is based on Psalm 51, please read the psalm before reading the chapter.

1. Personal comments/questions on chapter 10:

2. When would Psalm 51 be especially meaningful to us?

3. Mention at least four things we can learn about sin/forgiveness from Psalm 51, according to chapter 10 of Promises. Add your own ideas too, if you'd like.

B. Bible Study

Last time you were asked to apply four "How to Study the Bible" questions to a particular psalm. Please use the space below to answer the questions. Be ready to read the psalm and share your answers with the class.

1. *Who is the author and what is the author's purpose in writing?* Try to find the author of the psalm and the situation on which the psalm is based; for purpose, look for the feelings which the psalmist expresses.

2. *To what audience is the original message addressed?* Check the heading of the psalm; if none is given, you may not be able to answer this question.

3. *What does this passage say about the covenant (partnership) between God and his people?* Does the psalm say anything about how we should live as God's

partners or about the kind of God we have? Does it refer to Christ, the fulfillment of the covenant?

4. *What is the literary style of this passage?* Find an especially clear or descriptive verse or two and tell why it's good. Look for comparison, parallelism, good description.

Summary: Complete this statement: This psalm could be especially meaningful to us when...

C. Worship

If you feel the need for God's forgiving love, pray David's prayer in Psalm 51, the first twelve verses.

For Next Time: Read chapter 11 of *Promises,* "Every Man, Every Woman." Learn how Job teaches us to handle our suffering. As usual, complete section A, as your instructor suggests.

Every Man, Every Woman

A. Chapter Review

This week we invite you to simply read chapter 11 and jot down any questions about human suffering which this chapter raises in your mind. Dr. Nederhood says that no one can escape human agony. That fact—set alongside of our belief in a just, loving, and almighty God—has prompted some of the most difficult questions Christians have struggled with.

B. Bible Study

A brief dramatization follows, using selections from the book of Job. Your instructor may ask you to listen to the dramatization on tape or to read it.

A transcript of the tape, segment 6, follows:

A dramatization of selections from Job taken from *The Living Bible*

Narrator: There lived in the land of Uz a man named Job—a good man who feared God and stayed away from evil. He had a large family of seven sons and three daughters, and was immensely wealthy, for he owned 7,000 sheep, 3,000 camels, 500 teams of oxen, 500 female donkeys, and employed many servants. He was, in fact, the richest cattleman in that entire area.

Every year when each of Job's sons had a birthday, he invited his brothers and sisters to his home for a celebration. On these occasions they would eat and drink with great merriment. When these birthday parties ended—and sometimes they lasted several days—Job would summon his children to him and sanctify them, getting up early in the morning and offering a burnt offering for each of them. For Job said, "Perhaps my sons have sinned and turned away from God in their hearts." This was Job's regular practice.

One day as the angels came to present themselves before the Lord, Satan, the Accuser, came with them. The Lord asked Satan:

Lord: Where have you come from?

Satan: From patrolling the earth.

Lord: Have you noticed my servant Job? He is the finest man in all the earth—a good man who fears God and will have nothing to do with evil.

Satan: Why shouldn't he, when you pay him so well? You have always protected him and his home and his property from all harm. You have prospered everything he does—look at how rich he is! No wonder he worships you! But just take away his wealth, and you'll see him curse you to your face!

Lord: You may do anything you like with his wealth, but don't harm him physically.

Narrator: So Satan went away; and sure enough, not long afterwards when Job's sons and daughters were dining at the oldest brother's house, tragedy struck. A messenger rushed to Job's home with this news: "Your oxen were plowing, with the donkeys feeding beside them, when the Sabeans raided us, drove away the animals and killed all the farmhands except me. I am the only one left."

While this messenger was still speaking, another arrived with more bad news: "The fire of God has fallen from heaven and burned up your sheep and all the herdsmen, and I alone have escaped to tell you."

Before this man finished, still another messenger rushed in: "Three bands of Chaldeans have driven off your camels and killed your servants, and I alone have escaped to tell you."

As he was still speaking, another arrived to say, "Your sons and daughters were feasting in their oldest brother's home, when suddenly a mighty wind swept in from the desert, and engulfed the house so that the roof fell in on them and all are dead; and I alone escaped to tell you."

Then Job stood up and tore his robe in grief and fell down upon the ground before God.

Job: I came naked from my mother's womb, and I shall have nothing when I die. The Lord gave me everything I had, and they were his to take away. Blessed be the name of the Lord.

Narrator: In all of this, Job did not sin or revile God. Now the angels came again to present themselves before the Lord, and Satan with them.

Lord: Where have you come from?

Satan: From patrolling the earth.

Lord: Well, have you noticed my servant Job? He is the finest man in all the earth—a good man who fears God and turns away from all evil. And he has kept his faith in me despite the fact that you persuaded me to let you harm him without any cause.

Satan: Skin for skin. A man will give anything to save his life. Touch his body with sickness and he will curse you to your face!

Lord: Do with him as you please; only spare his life.

Narrator: So Satan went out from the presence of the Lord and struck Job with a terrible case of boils from head to foot. Then Job took a broken piece of pottery to scrape himself, and sat among the ashes. His wife said to him,

Wife: Job, are you still trying to be godly when God has done all this to you? Curse him and die.

Job: You talk like some heathen woman. What? Shall we receive only pleasant things from the hand of God and never anything unpleasant?

Narrator: So in all this Job said nothing wrong.

When three of Job's friends heard of all the tragedy that had befallen him, they got in touch with each other and traveled from their homes to comfort and console him. Their names were Eliphaz the Temanite, Bildad the Shuhite, and Zophar the Naamathite. Job was so changed that they could scarcely recognize him. Wailing loudly in despair, they tore their robes and threw dust into the air and put earth on their heads to demonstrate their sorrow. Then they sat upon the ground with him silently for seven days and nights, no one speaking a word; for they saw that his suffering was too great for words.

At last Job spoke, and cursed the day of his birth.

Job: Let the day of my birth be cursed, and the night when I was conceived. Let that day be forever forgotten. Let it be lost even to God, shrouded in eternal darkness. Why is a man allowed to be born if God is only going to give him a hopeless life of uselessness and frustration? I cannot eat for sighing; my groans pour out like water. What I always feared has happened to me. I was not fat and lazy, yet trouble struck me down.

Narrator: A reply to Job from Eliphaz the Temanite:

Eliphaz: At such a time as this should not trust in God still be your confidence? Shouldn't you believe that God will care for those who are good? Stop and think! Have you ever known a truly good and innocent person who was punished?

My advice to you is this: Go to God and confess your sins to him.

Job: One should be kind to a fainting friend, but you have accused me without the slightest fear of God. My brother, you have proved as unreliable as a brook; it floods when there is ice and snow, but in hot weather, disappears.

Stop assuming my guilt, for I am righteous. Don't be so unjust. Don't I know the difference between right and wrong? Would I not admit it if I had sinned?

Narrator: Bildad the Shuhite replies to Job:

Bildad: How long will you go on like this, Job, blowing words around like wind? Does God twist justice? If your children sinned against him, and he punished them, and you begged Almighty God for them—if you were pure and good, he would hear your prayer, and answer you, and bless you with a happy home. And though you started with little, you would end with much.

Job: Sure, I know all that. You're not telling me anything new. But how can a man be truly good in the eyes of God? If God decides to argue with him, can a man answer even one question of a thousand he asks? For God is so wise and so mighty. Who has ever opposed him successfully?

I am weary of living. Let me complain freely. I will speak in my sorrow and bitterness. I will say to God, "Don't just condemn me—tell me *why* you are doing it. Does it really seem right to you to oppress and despise me, a man you have made; and to send joy and prosperity to the wicked? Are you unjust like men? Is your life so short that you must hound me for sins you know full well I've not committed? Is it because you know no one can save me from your hand?"

Narrator: Zophar the Naamathite replies to Job:

Zophar: Shouldn't someone stem this torrent of words? Is a man proved right by all this talk? Should I remain silent while you boast? When you mock God, shouldn't someone make you ashamed? You claim you are pure in the eyes of God! Oh, that God would speak and tell you what he thinks! Oh, that he would make you truly see yourself, for he knows everything you've done. Listen! God is doubtless punishing you far less than you deserve!

Before you turn to God and stretch out your hands to him, get

Job: rid of your sins and leave all that iniquity behind you. Only then can you forget your misery. It will all be in the past. And your life will be cloudless; any darkness will be as bright as morning!

Job: Yes, I realize you know everything! All wisdom will die with you! Well, I know a few things myself—you are no better than I am. And who doesn't know these things you've been saying? I, the man who begged God for help, and God answered him, have become a laughingstock to my neighbors. Yes, I, a righteous man, am now the man they scoff at.

Be silent now and let me alone, that I may speak—and I am willing to face the consequences. Yes, I will take my life in my hand and say what I really think. God may kill me for saying this—in fact, I expect him to. Nevertheless, I am going to argue my case with him.

This is my case: *I know that I am righteous.* Who can argue with me over this? If you could prove me wrong I would stop defending myself and die.

Narrator: Job's three friends made more speeches, all with the same point. The friends tried to convince Job he was suffering because of his sin, and Job continued to say he was innocent. Then Job said:

Job: What wonderful helpers you all are! And how you have encouraged me in my great need! What wise things you have said! How did you ever think of all these brilliant comments?

I vow by the living God, who has taken away my rights, that as long as I live, while I have breath from God, my lips shall speak no evil, my tongue shall speak no lies. I will never, never agree that you are right; until I die I will vow my innocence. I am *not* a sinner—I repeat it again and again. My conscience is clear for as long as I live.

Narrator: After a final speech by a young man named Elihu, the Lord answered Job from the whirlwind:

Lord: Why are you using your ignorance to deny my providence? Now get ready to fight, for I am going to demand some answers from you, and you must reply.

Where were you when I laid the foundations of the earth? Tell me, if you know so much. Do you know how its dimensions were determined, and who did the surveying? What supports its foundations, and who laid its cornerstone, as the morning stars sang together and all the angels shouted for joy? Have you ever once commanded the morning to appear and caused the dawn to rise in the east?

Do you still want to argue with the Almighty? Or will you yield? Do you—God's critic—have the answers?

Job: I am nothing—how could I ever find the answers? I lay my hand upon my mouth in silence. I have said too much already.

I know that you can do anything and that no one can stop you. You ask who it is who has so foolishly denied your providence. It is I. I was talking about things I knew nothing about and did not understand, things far too wonderful for me. I loathe myself and repent in dust and ashes.

Narrator: After the Lord had finished speaking with Job, he said to Eliphaz the Temanite:

Lord: I am angry with you and with your two friends, for you have not been right in what you have said about me, as my servant Job was. Now go to my servant Job and offer a burnt offering for yourselves; and my servant Job will pray for you, and I will accept his prayer on your behalf, and won't destroy you as I should because of your sin, your failure to speak rightly concerning my servant Job.

Narrator: So Eliphaz the Temanite, and Bildad the Shuhite, and Zophar the Naamathite did as the Lord commanded them, and the Lord accepted Job's prayer on their behalf. Then, when Job prayed for his friends, the Lord restored his wealth and happiness! In fact, the Lord gave him twice as much as before! Then all of his brothers, sisters, and former friends arrived and feasted with him in his home, consoling him for all his sorrow, and comforting him because of all the trials the Lord had brought upon him. And each of them brought him a gift of money, and a gold ring.

So the Lord blessed Job at the end of his life more than at the beginning. For now he had 14,000 sheep, 6,000 camels, 1,000 teams of oxen, and 1,000 female donkeys.

God also gave him seven more sons and three more daughters. And in all the land there were no other girls as lovely as the daughters of Job; and their father put them into his will along with their brothers.

Job lived 140 years after that, living to see his grandchildren and great-grandchildren too. Then at last he died, an old, old man, after living a long, good life.

Dramatization taken directly from the following passages in *The Living Bible*:
1:1–6 Narrator
1:7–12 God and Satan dialogue
1:13–20 Narrator

1:21 Job
1:22–2:1 Narrator
2:2–6 2nd dialogue between God and Satan
2:7–8 Narrator
2:9 Wife
2:10 Job
2:11–3:1 Narrator
3:2–4, 23–26 Job
4:1 Narrator
4:6–8; 5:8 Eliphaz
6:14–18, 29–30 Job
8:1 Narrator
8:2–7 Bildad
9:2–4; 10:1–7 Job
11:1 Narrator
11:2–6, 13–14, 16–17 Zophar
12:1–4; 13:15, 18 Job

Narrator
26:1–4; 27:1–6 Job
38:1 Narrator
38:2–7, 12; 40:2–3 God
40:4–5; 42:2, 3, 6 Job
42:7a Narrator
42:7b–8 God
42:9–16 Narrator

Discussion questions for Job

1. What kind of person was Job, according to God (1:8)? According to Satan, why was Job this way (1:9–11; 2:4–5)? Do you think Satan's accusations could apply to Christians today?

2. What did Job's three friends say caused Job's suffering (4:6–9; 8:2–7; 11:1–6, 13–14)? What were Job's reactions to his friends' comments (12:1–4; 13:15,

65

18; 34:5–6)? Does Job's's defense strike you as accurate or presumptuous? How would you react if your friends said you were suffering because of some terrible sin you did?

3. Why was Job suffering? Did God give a complete and satisfactory explanation to his covenant partner? Did God prove to Job that he was good and just (38:2–7; 40:1–4; 42:1–6)?

4. Of what, exactly, did Job repent (42:1–6)?

5. According to the book of Job, how do hard times affect a covenant partner? Why do God's covenant partners continue to serve God in the midst of suffering?

6. What should be our attitude toward our own suffering?

C. Worship

Reflect on Romans 8:38–39 as a statement of faith in God:
I am sure that neither death, nor life, nor angels, nor principalities,
nor things present, nor things to come, nor powers, nor height, nor depth,
nor anything else in all creation, will be able to separate us from the
love of God in Christ Jesus our Lord.

And offer this prayer of David (Ps. 20:1–2) for the suffering:
The Lord answer you in the day of trouble!
The name of the God of Jacob protect you!
May he send you help from the sanctuary,
and give you support from Zion!

For Next Time: "That was stupid!" No one has escaped hearing and feeling that
statement. Chapter 12 of *Promises* says the Bible recognizes that problem. Read
the chapter and complete section A, as assigned, for next week.

Session Guide 12

Corvair in the Air

A. Chapter Review

1. Personal comments/questions on chapter 12:

2. What books make up the "wisdom literature" of the Bible?

3. Chapter 12 says the Bible's proverbs are different from others. The Bible's wisdom is "wisdom with a capital W." What does the author mean by that?

4. Briefly state Dr. Nederhood's view of the Song of Solomon and Ecclesiastes.

B. Bible Study

Today we'll apply a fifth "How to Study the Bible" question. Take a minute to jot down the first four, please:

1.

2.

3.

4.

The fifth question is

WHAT IS THE MEANING OF THE KEY WORD(S) IN THIS PASSAGE?

Sometimes the "word" may be a phrase like "Son of man" or "in Christ." To understand the meaning of a key word or phrase is helpful in understanding a passage.

Today you're asked to discover the meaning of the key word *wisdom*, as used in Proverbs 8. Work with others in your group to answer *one* of the following:

1. *Find synonyms for the key word.* What is wisdom like?

2. *Find contrasts to determine what the key word is not like.* Compare *wisdom* to other terms that are closely and not so closely related to it. How do these contrasts sharpen and define the nature of wisdom?

3. Find action words (verbs) which follow the key word to determine what the key word does. What does wisdom do?

4. Look for references to time or place to determine the history of the key word, where it came from. Where did wisdom come from (see vv. 22–31)?

Summary (to be done after the groups report): What is the meaning of the key word in this passage?
Attempt to write a brief answer to the above, indicating what wisdom means.

C. Worship

A prayer for understanding (wisdom) from Psalm 119:34–35, 73, 105, 125, 144, 169, 171 (NIV)

O Lord,

Give me understanding, and I will keep your law
　　and obey it with all my heart.

Direct me in the path of your commands,
　　for there I find delight.

Your hands made me and formed me;
　　give me understanding to learn your commands.

Your word is a lamp to my feet
　　and a light for my path.

I am your servant;
　　give me discernment . . .

Give me understanding
　　that I may live.

May my cry come before you, O Lord;
　　give me understanding according to your word.

My my lips overflow with praise,
　　for you teach me your decrees.
　　　　　　　　　Amen

For Next Time: Read chapter 13. "Seventeen in Samaria" discusses people who looked beautiful and went to the right churches. In that society, Amos was out of step. Read the chapter to find out why. Complete section A, as assigned.

Seventeen in Samaria

A. Chapter Review

This week we'll be looking at chapter 13 at the end of the class session. If you have specific questions about chapter 13, please jot them below:

B. Bible Study

Listen to these words from the prophet Amos.

A transcript of the tape, segment 7, follows:

Narrator: The following selections are taken from the book of Amos, Revised Standard Version.

These are the words of Amos, who was among the shepherds of Tekoa, which he saw concerning Israel in the days of Uzziah king of Judah and in the days of Jereboam the son of Joash, king of Israel (1:1).

THUS SAYS THE LORD:
"You only have I known
  of all the families of the earth;
therefore I will punish you
  for all your iniquities.
For three transgressions of Israel,
  and for four, I will not revoke the punishment;
because they sell the righteous for silver,
  and the needy for a pair of shoes—
they that trample the head of the poor into the
    dust of the earth,
  and turn aside the way of the afflicted."
                                    (3:2; 2:6–7)

THUS SAYS THE LORD:
"Hear this word, you cows of Bashan,
  who are in the mountains of Samaria,
who oppress the poor, who crush the needy,
  who say to their husbands,
    'Bring, that we may drink!'
The Lord God has sworn by his holiness
  that, behold, the days are coming upon you,
when they shall take you away with hooks,
  even the last of you with fishhooks..."
                                                    says the Lord.
                                                    (4:1-2)

Seek the Lord and live....
O you who turn justice to wormwood,
  and cast down righteousness to the earth!
                                                    (5:6-7)

For I know how many are your transgressions,
  and how great are your sins—
you who afflict the righteous, who take a bribe,
  and turn aside the needy in the gate.

Seek good, and not evil,
  that you may live;
and so the Lord, the God of hosts, will be with
  you....
Hate evil, and love good,
  and establish justice in the gate;
it may be that the Lord, the God of hosts,
  will be gracious to the remnant of Joseph.
                                                    (5:12, 14-15)

THUS SAYS THE LORD:
"I hate, I despise your feasts,
  and I take no delight in your solemn assemblies.
Even though you offer me your burnt offerings
and cereal offerings,
  I will not accept them,
and the peace offerings of your fatted beasts
  I will not look upon.
Take away from me the noise of your songs;
  to the melody of your harps I will not listen.
But let justice roll down like waters,
  and righteousness like an everflowing stream."
                                                    (5:21-24)

74

"Woe to those who are at ease in Zion,
and to those who feel secure on the mountain of
Samaria...."

(6:1)

THUS SAYS THE LORD:
"I will restore the fortunes of my people Israel,
  and they shall rebuild the ruined cities and in-
  habit them;
they shall plant vineyards and drink their wine,
  and they shall make gardens and eat their fruit.
I will plant them upon their land,
  and they shall never again be plucked up
  out of the land which I have given them,"

says the Lord your God.
(9:14-15)

Work on these five "How to Study the Bible" questions, please:

1. *What is the literary style of this book?* Amos is prophecy—God's word to the
   people. What form is prophecy usually written in? What obviously shows
   that Amos is writing God's words, not his own? Also, find verses which
   show that prophecy warns sinners, yet offers hope for those who trust in
   God. Is it correct to say that prophecy is concerned only with predicting the
   future?

2. *To what audience is the original message addressed?* What kind of people is Amos talking to? Support with chapter and verse references.

3. *Who is the author and what is the author's purpose in writing?* What have you learned about Amos from the selections just read? Which verses best express his reason for prophesying, for writing?

4. *What are the meanings of the key words in this passage?* Pick out some words which Amos emphasizes. Tell briefly what these words or phrases mean.

5. *What does this passage say about the covenant (partnership) between God and his people?* What kind of partner was Israel? How did God react to this?

C. Worship

In chapter 13, Dr. Nederhood finds God's emphasis on justice and righteousness "extremely upsetting." Why? What are your own feelings, after hearing from Amos?

Express some of these feelings to each other...and then to God, in silent prayer.

For Next Time: Read chapter 14, "Prophet to an Age of Madness." In addition, you may be asked to read a short passage from Jeremiah and answer these two questions:

—What is the passage generally about?
—What does it show about Jeremiah the prophet?

Prophet to an Age of Madness

A. Chapter Review

1. Personal comments/questions on chapter 14:

2. How does Dr. Nederhood describe Jeremiah's audience? Is today's world like that?

3. What was Jeremiah's basic message?

4. In addition to gloomy forecasts of captivity, Jeremiah also "turned on the light of the covenant." What does this mean? Mention one place in his book where Jeremiah does this.

B. Bible Study

You were asked last week (or will be asked today) to answer two questions about one of the following passages from Jeremiah. The questions are

—What is the passage generally about?
—What does it show about Jeremiah the prophet?

The passages are

1. Jeremiah 1:4–12
   Notes:

2. Jeremiah 11:1–11, 21–23
   Notes:

3. Jeremiah 20:1–13
   Notes:

4. Jeremiah 38
   Notes:

5. Jeremiah 39:1–14
   Notes:

6. Jeremiah 43:1–7 and 44:11–16
   Notes:

For General Discussion

Jeremiah 31:31–34 is an important passage on the covenant (it's quoted in Hebrews 8:8–12). What familiar covenantal promise of God can you find in this "new covenant" description? Who is going to bring the new covenant? In what way is the new covenant "written on our hearts"?

Do you think Jeremiah was a "success"? What's the key quality to being successful in God's sight?

C. Worship

A reading adapted from *Are You Joking, Jeremiah?* by Norman C. Habel

Reader 1:   God is way out there,
and he doesn't hang around
the way we like to do.

Reader 2:   And this brand-new covenant of God
is supposed to be a plan
Where everyone is perfect
and knows God man to man?

Reader 3:   We could never be like that!
We could never make the grade.
We are normal!
We are real!
Don't try and make us phonies.
Don't try and make us feel
As if we should be holy Joes.

Reader 4:   We'd never make it, Jeremiah.
God only knows.

Reader 5:   Are you fooling, Jeremiah?
Aren't you rather out of line?
For we don't know our God like that,
Not us, not like that.

Reader 6:   Hold on just a minute...
Someone's talking—Someone up there...
Listen...

Reader 7:   Why jump on Jeremiah?
Why beat him in the ground?
Don't you ever dream
Or have high expectations?
Have you ever tried
to understand
Just where God's plan was going?

Reader 8:   For I, you see
I am the Way,
The Hope of Jeremiah.

I am the Dream,
the life of his tomorrow,
The new Bond,
The New Cord,
The New Covenant
That unites new people with God.

Reader 9: If for a moment
You can feel yourself alone,
Torn free from all the moorings.
Cut off from all the ties
With humanity and God
That give life meaning—
If you can see your selfish self
Floating off alone
Because you love only your world...
Then perhaps the dream
of a new bond made by God,
A new covenant of life,
Which you certainly don't deserve,
May not be quite so strange.

Reader 10: So if you're not too proud
Too busy,
Or too old,
I will throw you my forgiveness
As I did when they coldly nailed me
To the splintered stake of death.
My forgiveness reaches out
As you hear me cry, "You're in,"
As you see me sweat and die
For all the broken ties
Between humanity and me.

I'm waiting for you
To take my forgiveness
and mend the ties
that you have broken
And others too have broken.
I'm waiting.

From *Are You Joking, Jeremiah?* by Norman C. Habel.
Copyright 1967 and reprinted by courtesy of The Walther League.

For Next Time: Please read chapter 15 and the book of Esther.

Session Guide 15

Prisoners of War

A. Chapter Review

Please use chapter 15 to complete the following statements:

1. Judah was taken captive by the nation of _____.

2. The tragedy of captivity was increased because _____

_____.

3. Three Bible books written about God's people in exile are _____,

_____, and_____.

4. The book of Esther, taken out of its biblical context, could be considered pretty

good material for _____!

5. "The exile was a horrible but cleansing process that flushed idolatry out of their

souls..." page 71). One example of how God's people were "cleansed" is ___

_____

_____.

6. "The exile was one means by which God brought his grace." This statement

(page 73) means _____

_____

_____.

B. Bible Study

1. Review

Because Esther has an interesting and involved plot, it's easy to forget the details, even if you've read the book recently. Try putting these plot items in the order in which they happened—write *1* by the first item, and so on. Use your Bible if you wish.

_____ King Ahasuerus gives a very expensive, week-long party.

_____ Haman is hung on the gallows he built for Mordecai; Mordecai gets everything that belonged to Haman and becomes the second most powerful man in the kingdom.

_____ Esther persuades the king to revoke the order to kill all the Jews. Mordecai sends letters to all the Jews, who rejoice!

_____ Esther, following Mordecai's advice, asks an audience with the king. She then invites the king and Haman to dinner.

_____ Haman gets a big promotion from the king; then, because Mordecai refuses to bow down to him, Haman determines to destroy all the Jews.

_____ The Jews destroy their enemies and celebrate on the feast days called Purim.

_____ Queen Vashti disobeys the king; he begins the search for a new queen.

_____ The king and Haman attend Esther's second banquet; Esther names Haman as the man who would kill her and her people.

_____ Esther wins the king's beauty contest and becomes queen in place of Vashti.

_____ Haman, fresh from his first banquet with the king and queen, spots Mordecai and is so angered he builds a huge gallows on which to hang him.

_____ The king honors Mordecai for an earlier act; Haman is forced to participate in the honoring ceremonies.

2. Study—the Book of Esther

Esther is a unusual book—in fact, it may seem strange that it's included in the Bible. God is not mentioned in the entire book, nor is the covenant, prayer, miracles, or prophecy. Even the fantastic escape of God's people seems only the work of two courageous—though not very religious—human beings. Esther herself says not one word of thanks to God for delivering tens of thousands of Jews from death.

Still, we believe the Holy Spirit led the early church to include this book as part of the Bible (canon). It has something to say to us. The unknown author wrote it with some purpose in mind. What *was* the author's purpose?

Below are two different answers to that question. Choose the one you think is the best answer. Jot down the reasons for your choice.

Answer 1

The purpose of Esther was to show how God kept his covenant people safe, so that someday a Savior would be born to their descendants. Even when Israel and Judah were led away into captivity, God promised that a faithful remnant would return to their homeland and continue the covenant line. The book of Esther shows how God used two courageous Jews, Esther and Mordecai, to save his covenant people. Mordecai knew God would somehow save his people: "Think not [he said to Esther] that in the king's palace you will escape any more than all the other Jews. For if you keep silence at such a time as this, relief and deliverance will rise for the Jews from another quarter, but you and your father's house will perish. And who knows whether you have not come to the kingdom for such a time as this?" (4:13–14)

Answer 2

The purpose of Esther was to give people of all times two shining examples of courage and goodness. Esther risked her life to save her people (4:16). From her we can learn to face with courage those who persecute God's people and try to undermine the church. Mordecai refused to give in to the evil Haman, and eventually became the most important man in the kingdom (10:3), while evil Haman was hanged from his own gallows. Mordecai teaches us that those who seek to hurt God's people will only destroy themselves.

Notes:

C. Worship

Open your Bibles to Psalm 126. Imagine yourself having been in prison for years in a foreign country, prevented from even praying to God, having heard no songs of praise to the Lord for years, but now having just been told you will be going home tomorrow.

Read this psalm in unison with that feeling in your heart.

For Next Time: "The Wet Congregation and the Gloomy Bartender"—what a strange title for a chapter about the Bible! Read chapter 16 of *Promises* for next time to see which two men the author is talking about. As usual, complete section A, as assigned by your instructor. Try also to read the selections from Nehemiah listed at the end of chapter 15.

The Wet Congregation and the Gloomy Bartender

A. Chapter Review

1. Personal comments/questions on chapter 16:

2. Explain the title—who was the wet congregation and who was the gloomy bartender? What did each do?

3. Dr. Nederhood says that the exiles' return home reminds him of an important truth about God. What truth is that? How can knowing that truth help us when we learn of world-shaking events through TV, radio, or newspaper?

B. Bible Study

1. Read Nehemiah 2, then discuss these two "How to Study the Bible" questions:
   a. *Who is the author and what is the author's purpose in writing?*

   b. *What is the literary style of this passage?* Is there anything unusual about the way it's written?

2. Read Nehemiah 4, then discuss these two "How to Study the Bible" questions:
   a. *What are the meanings of the key words in this passage?* What key words describing God's people are frequently used in this passage? How are God's people pictured?

   b. *What does this passage (Nehemiah 2 and 4) tell us about the covenant (partnership) between God and his people?*

3. T. S. Eliot has written a poem about Nehemiah and the rebuilding of Jerusalem. But the poem is also about how the church builds today. Listen to the poem (which follows) and then discuss the following:
   a. any lines you don't understand.
   b. the "lions" against which the church needs to defend itself today.
   c. the "builders" of today's church. Who are they, and how do they build?

A transcript of the tape, segment 8, follows:

Readings from "Choruses from 'The Rock'" by T. S. Eliot

Chorus of Workmen (*several voices chanting in unison*):
In the vacant places
We will build with new bricks
There are hands and machines
And clay for new brick
And lime for new mortar
Where the bricks are fallen
We will build with new stone
Where the beams are rotten
We will build with new timbers
Where the word is unspoken
We will build with new speech
There is work together
A Church for all
And a job for each
Every man to his work.

First Voice:
There are those who would build the Temple,
And those who prefer that the Temples should not be
    built.
In the days of Nehemiah the Prophet
There was no exception to the general rule.
In Shushan the palace, in the month Nisan,
He served the wine to the King Artaxerxes,
And he grieved for the broken city, Jerusalem;
And the King gave him leave to depart
That he might rebuild the city.
So he went, with a few, to Jerusalem,
And there, by the dragon's well, by the dung gate,
By the fountain gate, by the king's pool,
Jerusalem lay waste, consumed with fire;
No place for a beast to pass.
There were enemies without to destroy him,
And spies and self-seekers within,
When he and his men laid their hands to rebuild-
    ing the wall.
So they built as men must build
With the sword in one hand and the trowel in the
    other.

Second Voice:
O Lord, deliver me from the man of excellent
intention and impure heart: for the heart is deceit-
ful above all things, and desperately wicked.
Sanballat the Horonite and Tobiah the Ammonite
and Geshem the Arabian: were doubtless men of
public spirit and zeal.
Preserve me from the enemy who has something to
gain: and from the friend who has something to
lose.
Remembering the words of Nehemiah the Prophet:
"The trowel in hand, and the gun rather loose in
the holster."

The man who has builded during the day would
return to his hearth at nightfall: to be blessed with
the gift of silence, and doze before he sleeps.
But we are encompassed with snakes and dogs: therefore some must labour, and others must hold the
spears.

Third Voice:
It is hard for those who have never known
persecution,
And who have never known a Christian,
To believe these tales of Christian persecution.
It is hard for those who live near a Bank
To doubt the security of their money.
It is hard for those who live near a Police Station
To believe in the triumph of violence.
Do you think that the Faith has conquered the
World
And that lions no longer need keepers?
Do you need to be told that whatever has been, can still be?

Why should men love the Church? Why should they
love her laws?
She tells them of Life and Death, and of all that
they would forget.
She is tender where they would be hard, and hard
where they like to be soft.
She tells them of Evil and Sin, and other unpleasant
facts.
They constantly try to escape
From the darkness outside and within

By dreaming of systems so perfect that no one will
  need to be good.
But the man that is will shadow
The man that pretends to be.
And the Son of Man was not crucified once for all,
The blood of the martyrs not shed once for all,
The lives of the Saints not given once for all,
But the Son of Man is crucified always
And there shall be Martyrs and Saints.
And if blood of Martyrs is to flow on the steps
We must first build the steps;
And if the Temple is to be cast down
We must first build the Temple.

Chorus of Workmen (*repeat of opening lines*):
In the vacant places...

C. Worship

As you think about the gifts God has given you and others in your congregation—gifts to help build and defend the church—make these lines your prayer:

Lord, shall we not bring these gifts to Your service?
Shall we not bring to Your service all our powers
For life, for dignity, grace and order...?
The Lord who created us must wish us to create
And employ our creation again in His service....
We thank Thee for our little light....
We thank Thee who hast moved us to building, to finding, to forming....
O Light Invisible, we give Thee thanks for Thy great glory.
                                        Amen.

For Next Time: You would think that the exiles, upon their return to Jerusalem, would never again disobey the Lord after all their suffering. "The Liberated Wailing Wall" shows how they forgot. Read it for next time; it's chapter 17 in *Promises*. And complete section A, as assigned.

The Liberated Wailing Wall

A. Chapter Review

1. What happened to those who returned from exile? In other words, what kind of people did Haggai, Zechariah, and Malachi prophesy to?

2. What were the messages of these prophets?

3. Dr. Nederhood says that Zechariah talks about "that day." Malachi too prophesies a coming "day of the Lord." In Malachi 4:5 we read, "Behold, I will send you Elijah the prophet before the great and terrible day of the Lord comes." What do you think is meant by "day of the Lord," and who was "Elijah"?

B. Bible Study

1. Read Malachi 3 and 4. In the columns provided, write down all the details of Christ's coming that seem pleasant and welcome ("great") and those details that seem "terrible" and perhaps painful. Mark the verse number next to the phrase that you write.

GREAT	TERRIBLE

2. In the New Testament, the "day of the Lord" refers to the *second* coming of Jesus. Again, read the following New Testament passages and write down details in the appropriate columns that show the judgment day as both "great" and "terrible."

GREAT

1 Thessalonians 5:1–6

2 Peter 3:10

Matthew 24:29–31

Revelation 20:11–21:4

TERRIBLE

1 Thessalonians 5:1–6

2 Peter 3:10

Matthew 24:29–31

Revelation 20:11–21:4

3. What do you think of the coming day of the Lord? Should you look at it as Malachi did, with joy and fear, as a great *and* terrible day? Or should you think only of the "great" things about that day?

C. Worship

The Heidelberg Catechism asks this question about Christ's second coming: "How does Christ's return 'to judge the living and the dead' comfort you?" Read or reflect on this answer:

In all my distress and persecution
I turn my eyes to the heavens
and confidently await as judge the very One
who has already stood trial in my place before God
and so has removed the whole curse from me.
All his enemies and mine
he will condemn to everlasting punishment:
but me and all his chosen ones
he will take along with him
into the joy and the glory of heaven.

(Answer 52)

For Next Time: "Oh, Susanna!" is a chapter about the Apocrypha, those books between the two testaments in the Bible. Why are they in some Bibles and not in others? Read chapter 18 from *Promises* for next time to get the answer. As usual, work on section A, as assigned.

Oh, Susanna!

A. Chapter Review

1. What does *apocrypha* mean? Use a dictionary to find its original meaning and what it has come to mean today.

2. List some of the Apocrypha books (see chapter 18).

3. When were these books written?

4. Why are these books worth reading, according to Dr. Nederhood?

5. Deduce from chapter 18 some reasons why these books aren't accepted as part of the canon (list of authentic Bible books).

6. Do you have any additional questions about the Apocrypha?

B. Apocrypha Study

Below is a transcript of the tape, segment 9, a selection from the Apocrypha which will be used instead of the regular Bible study. Read the passage; then complete the exercise which follows.

Bel and the Dragon (an apocryphal addition to the book of Daniel)
When King Astyages was laid with his fathers, Cyrus the Persian received his kingdom. [2]And Daniel was a companion of the king, and was the most honored of his friends.

[3]Now the Babylonians had an idol called Bel, and every day they spent on it twelve bushels of fine flour and forty sheep and fifty gallons of wine. [4]The king revered it and went every day to worship it. But Daniel worshiped his own God.

[5]And the king said to him, "Why do you not worship Bel?" He answered, "Because I do not revere man-made idols, but the living God, who created heaven and earth and has dominion over all flesh."

[6]The king said to him, "Do you not think that Bel is a living God? Do you not see how much he eats and drinks every day?" [7]Then Daniel laughed, and said, "Do not be deceived, O king; for this is but clay inside and brass outside, and it never ate or drank anything."

[8]Then the king was angry, and he called his priests and said to them, "If you do not tell me who is eating these provisions, you shall die. [9]But if you prove that Bel is eating them, Daniel shall die, because he blasphemed against Bel." And Daniel said to the king, "Let it be done as you have said."

[10]Now there were seventy priests of Bel, besides their wives and children. And the king went with Daniel into the temple of Bel. [11]And the priests of Bel said, "Behold, we are going outside; you yourself, O king, shall set forth the food and mix and place the wine, and shut the door and seal it with your signet. [12]And when you return in the morning, if you do not find that Bel has eaten it all, we will die; or else Daniel will, who is telling lies about us." [13]They were unconcerned, for beneath the table they had made a hidden entrance, through which they used to go in regularly and consume the provisions. [14]When they had gone out, the king set forth the food for Bel. Then Daniel ordered his servants to bring ashes and they sifted them throughout the whole temple in the presence of the king alone. Then they went out, shut the door and sealed it with the king's signet, and departed. [15]In the night the priests came with their wives and children, as they were accustomed to do, and ate and drank everything.

[16]Early in the morning the king rose and came, and Daniel with him. [17]And the king said, "Are the seals unbroken, Daniel?" He answered, "They are unbroken, O king." [18]As soon as the doors were opened, the king looked at the table, and shouted in a loud voice, "You are great, O Bel; and with you there is no deceit, none at all."

[19]Then Daniel laughed, and restrained the king from going in, and said,

"Look at the floor, and notice whose footsteps these are." 20The king said, "I see footsteps of men and women and children."

21Then the king was enraged, and he seized the priests and their wives and children; and they showed him the secret doors through which they were accustomed to enter and devour what was on the table. 22Therefore the king put them to death, and gave Bel over to Daniel, who destroyed it and its temple.

23There was also a great dragon, which the Babylonians revered. 24And the king said to Daniel, "You cannot deny that this is a living god; so worship him." 25Daniel said, "I will worship the Lord my God, for he is the living God. 26But if you, O king, will give me permission, I will slay the dragon without sword or club." The king said, "I give you permission."

27Then Daniel took pitch, fat, and hair, and boiled them together and made cakes, which he fed to the dragon. The dragon ate them, and burst open. And Daniel said, "See what you have been worshiping!"

28When the Babylonians heard it, they were very indignant and conspired against the king, saying, "The king has become a Jew; he has destroyed Bel, and slain the dragon, and slaughtered the priests." 29Going to the king, they said, "Hand Daniel over to us, or else we will kill you and your household." 30The king saw that they were pressing him hard, and under compulsion he handed Daniel over to them.

31They threw Daniel into the lions' den, and he was there for six days. 32There were seven lions in the den, and every day they had been given two human bodies and two sheep; but these were not given to them now, so that they might devour Daniel.

33Now the prophet Habakkuk was in Judea. He had boiled pottage and had broken bread in a bowl, and was going into the field to take it to the reapers. 34But the angel of the Lord said to Habakkuk, "Take the dinner which you have to Babylon, to Daniel, in the lions' den." 35Habakkuk said, "Sir I have never seen Babylon, and I know nothing about the den." 36Then the angel of the Lord took him by the crown of his head, and lifted him by his hair and set him down in Babylon, right over the den, with the rushing sound of the wind itself.

37Then Habakkuk shouted, "Daniel, Daniel! Take the dinner which God has sent you." 38And Daniel said, "Thou hast remembered me, O God, and hast not forsaken those who love thee." 39So Daniel arose and ate. And the angel of God immediately returned Habakkuk to his own place.

40On the seventh day the king came to mourn for Daniel. When he came to the den he looked in, and there sat Daniel. 41And the king shouted with a loud voice, "Thou art great, O Lord God of Daniel, and there is no other besides thee." 42And he pulled Daniel* out, and threw into the den the men who had attempted his destruction, and they were devoured immediately before his eyes.

*Gk him

Imagine that you are a part of a Protestant church committee during Reformation times. You've just spent a week studying *Bel and the Dragon* and have decided that this addition to Daniel ought not to be part of the canon; however, you've also decided it could be profitably read by Christians for whatever spiritual value it has.

Now you must report to the leaders of the church. They want to know why you did not accept the book as part of the canon. They also want to know what possible benefit anyone could get from reading this book.

What are you going to tell them?

Notes:

C. Worship

The Apocrypha has sections that express open praise to God. This hymn of praise from the *Song of the Three Young Men* expresses the hope of the three men in the fiery furnace.

Bless the Lord, all works of the Lord.
Bless the Lord you sons of men.
Bless the Lord, O Israel.
Bless the Lord, you servants of the Lord.
Bless the Lord, you who are holy and humble in heart.
Bless the Lord...for he has rescued us from Hades and saved us from the hand of death.
Give thanks to the Lord, for he is good, for his mercy endures forever.

Amen.

For Next Time: "The Apostolic Quartet" is *not* a singing group. It is Matthew, Mark, Luke, and John. According to Dr. Nederhood, "our whole understanding of the Bible" hangs on the eyewitness accounts of these men. Read chapter 19 in *Promises* for next time, and complete section A, as assigned.

The Apostolic Quartet

A. Chapter Review

1. Personal comments/questions on chapter 19:

2. The four Gospels are something like a quartet in that they are in harmony. What is the central harmony (message) of the Gospels? Why are they so crucial?

3. Find a partial definition of the word *Gospels* on page 90. Copy the definition here, along with additional notes from your instructor.

4. How do you account for the differences between the Gospels?

B. Bible Study

Please take a few minutes to carefully read the chart on the following pages. It outlines some of the differences between the Gospels while showing that all the writers consistently point to Jesus Christ.

THE GOSPEL ACCORDING TO

MATTHEW   MARK

	MATTHEW	MARK
AUTHOR AND AUDIENCE	Wealthy tax collector who became a disciple. Wrote around A.D. 70-90, mainly for Jewish audience.	Not a disciple, but a friend of Peter and Paul. Was probably first Gospel writer (A.D. 70). Wrote to Christians suffering in Rome.
AUTHOR'S PURPOSE	**To present Jesus as the Messiah, the fulfillment of O.T. prophecy, the righteous King of the Jews (1:1).**	**To proclaim the good news of Christ in the context of the struggle between the kingdom of God and the kingdom of evil, a struggle that involves suffering and martyrdom.**
LITERARY STYLE	Very detailed; many references to O.T. prophecies which Christ fulfilled. Divides his Gospel into five parts, like the Jewish Torah, each part ending: "When Jesus finished his teaching..."	Concise and highly dramatic. Often uses term *immediately*. The shortest Gospel. Shows Christ as man of action who suffered much.
FIRST WORDS OF CHRIST	Matthew 3:15	Mark 1:15

LUKE	JOHN
Not a Jew or a disciple or an eyewitness, but a doctor who traveled with Paul. Wrote Luke and Acts (A.D. 70-90) for Gentile audience.	A disciple "whom Jesus loved." The last Gospel (after A.D. 90). Intended primarily for the church as a supplement to the other Gospels.
To present—in orderly fashion—Jesus Christ as the great healer and teacher who quietly and faithfully carried out his God-given task (1:1–4).	**To present Christ as the only One who can truly fill all human needs, so that people may believe he is the Christ, the Son of God (20:31).**
Warm, vivid, descriptive style, marked by compassion for sick and oppressed. Contains much not found in other Gospels.	Grand concepts (life, light). Polished and eloquent. Describes inner life and feelings of Christ. Two-thirds of book is on last six months of Christ's life.
Luke 2:49	John 1:38,39

Using the Chart

Working in small groups, look up the first words of Christ in the Gospel to which you are assigned. Then answer two questions:

1. Why did the author of this Gospel choose to record these words as the first words of Christ in his work? (Check the author's purpose in writing this Gospel.)

2. What is the meaning of Christ's words for our lives?

C. Worship

The last words of Christ, as recorded by Matthew, have special meaning for us. Look up these words (Matt. 28:18–20) and read them in unison.

For Next Time: Read "My Brother, Jesus" (chapter 20 in *Promises*) and complete section *A*, as assigned.

My Brother, Jesus

A. Chapter Review

1. Personal comments/questions on chapter 20:

2. Is the following series of statements correct? How is the conclusion related to Matthew 1 and the genealogy of Jesus?

   —Jesus is an adopted son of Abraham.
   —Believers are adopted children of Abraham.
   —Therefore Jesus is a brother to all believers.

3. How do the temptations of Jesus show that he is "our brother"?

4. Do you usually think of Jesus as your brother? Why or why not? How does Jesus act as a brother to us?

B. Bible Study

Jesus was led by the Spirit into the wilderness to be "tempted by the devil." There Jesus faced a test of obedience to God the Father—the same test all God's covenant partners face. Jesus stood in our place as God's covenant partner.

Read Matthew 4:1–11 and/or listen to a dramatization of that passage from the cassette (tape, segment 10). Afterwards, work with others in your group to answer four questions about one of the temptations:

1. Why would the temptation have been attractive to Christ?

2. What wrong attitude or action toward God as covenant partner did the temptation promote?

3. How did Israel fall into the same temptation which Christ resisted? (Look up the Old Testament passage—and its context—that Christ quoted to Satan.)

4. Give one modern example of the same type of temptation.

Please write your answers after the numbers, below.

First temptation: Matthew 4:1–4 and Deuteronomy 8:3

1.

2.

3.

4.

Second temptation: Matthew 4:5-7; Deuteronomy 6:16; Exodus 17:1-7

1.

2.

3.

4.

Third temptation: Matthew 4:8-11 and Deuteronomy 6:13

1.

2.

3.

4.

C. Worship

Every time we pray the Lord's Prayer, we ask God not to lead us into temptation but to deliver us from evil. The Heidelberg Catechism, Answer 127, explains what this request means. You may want to recite this answer together, as a prayer:

> *And lead us not into temptation,*
> *but deliver us from evil* means
>
> By ourselves we are too weak
> to hold our own even for a moment.
>
> And our sworn enemies—
>   the devil, the world, and our own flesh—
> never stop attacking us.
>
> And so, Lord,
> uphold us and make us strong
>   with the strength of your Holy Spirit,
> so that we may not go down to defeat
>   in this spiritual struggle,
> but may firmly resist our enemies
>   until we finally win the complete victory.

For Next Time: Read chapter 21 of *Promises* and complete section A, as assigned.

Crash Course in Christianity

A. Chapter Review

1. Personal comments/questions on chapter 21:

2. Complete the following statements, based on chapter 21:

   a. Mark's Gospel is an ideal "crash course" for Christians because

   _____

   _____ .

   b. Matthew presents Jesus as our brother; Mark presents him as _____ .

   c. The kingdom idea, as Mark develops it, focuses on the world-wide struggle

   between _____ and _____ .

   d. In Mark, the miracles Jesus performs are proof of his _____ .

   e. Mark, says Dr. Nederhood, teaches us three things about the demon world:

   first, that _____ ;

   second, that _____

   _____ ; and third, that _____

   _____ .

   f. Not only the demons are against Christ, according to Mark; Jesus must also

   do battle with _____ .

   g. The "most revolutionary principle of the kingdom," a requirement which

   puts down all pretensions of false religion, is _____

   _____ .

h. Mark's Gospel is an especially good book for tired, discouraged Christians

to read because _____

_____ .

B. Bible Study

To help us understand the meaning of the parable from Mark 12:1–11, we'll use a new "How to Study the Bible" question (number 6, below). But first, try recalling the five study questions already used. Exact wording isn't important—do try to remember the basic questions:

1.

2.

3.

4.

5.

6. WHAT IS THE CONTEXT OF THIS VERSE OR PASSAGE?

What does *context* mean? Imagine yourself walking into the hall after class and telling a friend, "That was so boring!" The teacher overhears you and thinks you're talking about his class. But in fact you were talking about a book your friend gave you to read. Taking the remark out of context (surrounding), the teacher misunderstands it.

Sometimes remarks are deliberately taken out of context—as, for example, when a dishonest movie ad quotes *Time* magazine as saying of an actor, "His best performance!" But the ad leaves out the context: "His best performance failed to save this disaster of a film." Sometimes the Bible is quoted out of context too. Some parents are fond of quoting Ephesians 6:1—"Children, obey your parents." But they ignore the context of the verse, which includes the warning "Fathers, do not provoke your children to anger" (Eph. 6:4). On the other hand, some children tend to ignore verse 1 in favor of verse 4.

Obviously, reading or hearing things in context is important. Generally, the context of a Bible verse or passage is that which precedes or follows the passage, revealing the setting of that passage. The context may also mean the nature of the book (its purpose, author, audience, etc.) in which the passage occurs.

For today's Bible study, we'll use our Bibles to understand—in context—the parable of the vineyard and the wicked tenants. Begin by reading the parable from Mark 12:1–11.

The Parable of the Vineyard—in Context

1. One context clue is the book in which the passage appears. Will it help us much to review Mark's purpose, audience, and so on, as related to this parable? Why or why not?

2. Skim Mark 11–13—especially the chapter headings—to find out what events in Jesus' life had just preceded and followed this parable.

3. Find out what you can about the audience of Christ's parable. Read Mark 11:27–33 and 12:1. To whom was Jesus speaking? About what? Read Mark 12:12. Who are "they," and why did they try to arrest Jesus?

4. How did Jesus' audience, in a sense, soon "act out" this parable?

5. In light of the context, what do you think Jesus was teaching in this parable?

6. How did your research on the context of the parable add to your understanding of it?

C. Worship

Parables are more than puzzles to be unlocked by careful reading and by studying the context. We have to see ourselves in the parables. Maybe reflecting on this poem will help us do that.

A transcript of the tape, segment 11, follows:

He Bore Our Griefs

No, it was not the Jews who crucified,
Nor who betrayed You in the judgment place,
Nor who, Lord Jesus, spat into Your face,
Nor who with buffets struck You as You died.
　No, it was not the soldiers fisted bold
Who lifted up the hammer and the nail,
Or raised the cursed cross on Calvary's hill,
Or, gambling, tossed the dice to win Your robe.
　I am the one, O Lord, who brought You there,
I am the heavy cross You had to bear,
I am the rope that bound You to the tree,
　The whip, the nail, the hammer, and the spear,
The blood-stained crown of thorns You had to wear:
It was my sin, alas, it was for me.

By Jacob Revius, trans. by Henrietta Ten Harmsel.
From *The Country of the Risen King* by Merle Meeter. Copyright 1978
by Baker Book House and used by permission of Wayne State University.

For Next Time: Find out what makes the Gospel of John stand apart. Read chapter 22, "The Special Gospel." Do section A, as assigned.

The Special Gospel

A. Chapter Review

1. Personal comments/questions on chapter 22:

2. How is the Gospel of John "special"? Write a few sentences answering this question, based on chapter 22 but also on your own reading from John.

B. Bible Study

Sometimes, when we hear stories about things we haven't seen for ourselves, we ask, "Were you there? Did you actually see it happen?" If the storyteller says, "Yes, I saw the whole thing," we tend to believe it, assuming we trust the storyteller. At least we'll listen to more details.

John's Gospel is an eye-witness account of Jesus' life, written by someone Jesus knew and loved. All through his Gospel John says, "I was a witness. I saw it." When one of the soldiers near the cross shoved a spear into Jesus' side, John says about himself, "He who saw it has borne witness—his testimony is true, and he knows that he tells the truth" (John 19:35).

But John didn't write down *everything* he saw. He selected his material care fully, for a definite purpose. You'll find that purpose clearly stated in John 20:31. Write that purpose here:

Every chapter in John's Gospel has verses which reflect this purpose. For today's Bible study, you'll be asked to concentrate on one chapter (or part of a chapter), and to jot down all the verses which relate to John's purpose. Read your assigned chapter; then make a list of key words and phrases, including the verse references where these are located. Remember, you're looking for words like *believe, Christ, Son of God, life.* You're looking for evidence that Jesus is the Messiah, the Son of God.
Notes:

C. Worship

Select a short passage from John which has special meaning for you, which you find comforting or helpful in some way. (John 1:1–18 and John 14 are passages which you can check if you wish.) Be ready to read your selection to the class for closing devotions.

For Next Time: Read about Luke, who was a doctor, a cultured Greek...and an unbeliever, in chapter 22 of *Promises*, "Our Heathen Friend." As usual, complete section A, as your instructor suggests.

Our Heathen Friend

A. Chapter Review

1. Personal comments/questions on chapter 23:

2. Write down the facts you learned about Luke (as a person) from chapter 23 and the Gospel Chart (session 19).

3. Why were miracles important to the early church?

4. If you were asked to write a book called *The Acts of Jesus Christ Today*, what two specific "acts" would you be sure to mention?

B. Bible Study

1. *Acts 1:1-11*
   a. Compare Acts 1:1 to Luke 1:1-4. How do we know Luke is the author of Acts?

b. According to Luke 1:1-4, what is his Gospel about? In what sense is Acts about the same thing? In what sense is it quite different? (See Acts 1:8.)

c. Acts 1:8 is the key to the whole book of Acts. It also says something very important about the covenant (partnership) between God and his people. What?

2. *Acts 11:1-26*

   a. Read verses 1-3. How did some early Christians regard the Gentiles? Do Christians today sometimes act clannish, unwilling to associate with other Christians?

   b. Read through verse 18. What convinced Peter and later the Jews in Jerusalem that Gentiles were part of the covenant?

c. Read verses 19–26. Find three things which helped extend the gospel to the Gentiles.

C. Worship

Reflect together on what Acts 11 says to us as modern Gentile Christians.

Then pray this prayer of Christ's, adapted from John 17:11, 17, 21:

Holy Father,
    In your name keep those whom you have given
        to Christ,
            that they may be one,
                even as the Father and the Son are one.

Sanctify them in the truth; your Word is truth.
May all those who believe in you,
    also be one with us and with you,
        so that the world will know
            Jesus is Lord.
                                    Amen

For Next Time: Read chapter 24 and complete section *A*, as assigned.

Don't Throw This Letter Away

A. Chapter Review

Check chapter 24 to determine whether the following statements about the
New Testament letters are true or false.

_____ 1. Twenty-one of the twenty-seven New Testament books are letters.

_____ 2. Much of what we believe comes from these letters.

_____ 3. The letters are also called "epistles" because they're intended to teach doctrine.

_____ 4. Paul, Peter, James, and John are the known authors of the letters in the New Testament.

_____ 5. As a group the epistles have few personal references from their writers.

_____ 6. The epistles ought to be read as statements of doctrine, not as personal letters addressed to specific audiences.

_____ 7. Romans, Paul's last letter, was written from a jail cell.

_____ 8. There are no obscure (unclear) passages in the epistles; God's holy Word is always crystal clear to us today.

_____ 9. The letter writers themselves claimed their messages had a divine origin.

_____ 10. Dr. Nederhood describes the letters as personal, historical, God-given, and true.

B. Bible Study

One of the shortest and most personal letters in the Bible is the book of
Philemon, only 25 verses long. It's Paul's letter—written from prison in

Rome—to Philemon, who once owned the slave Onesimus. Onesimus had run away to Rome, where he met Paul, became converted, and served Paul during his imprisonment. Had Onesimus been caught by one of the professional slave hunters of the day, he could legally have been beaten, sold, or even crucified.

Knowing that Philemon would likely treat Onesimus as a Christian brother, Paul persuaded Onesimus to return to Philemon (who had himself been converted by Paul and had worked with him in Colossae). With Onesimus Paul sent a letter which contained proof that Onesimus was a true disciple of Christ and therefore deserved kind acceptance.

That, briefly, was Paul's *purpose* in writing Philemon. Today's Bible study will look at the *audience* Paul's letter addressed.

The Opening Greeting (vv. 1–3)

How private a letter is this? Could Philemon feel free to share it with others, do you think?

Paul's greeting (v. 3) is his usual one and suggests to the audience that the letter is genuine.

Thanksgiving and Prayer (vv. 4–7)

What would Philemon find pleasing, comforting, and encouraging about this section of Paul's letter?

The Request (vv. 8–20)

(vv. 8–9)   What is Paul saying to Philemon here? On what does Paul base his appeal?

(v. 10)   What would this say (indirectly) to Philemon, who was bound to have some resentment toward his runaway slave?

(v. 11)   Paul is playing with Onesimus's name here (see the footnote in your Bible). How might Onesimus be "useful" to Philemon?

(vv. 12–13)   What impression would these verses give Philemon about Paul's attitude toward his runaway slave?

(v. 14)   What is Paul telling Philemon here?

(vv. 15–16)   How should Philemon treat Onesimus, according to Paul? Would Philemon think that Paul is telling him to free Onesimus? Is Paul coming out *for* or *against* the institution of slavery?

(v. 17)   What is Paul appealing to here to insure Christian treatment
            of Onesimus?

(vv. 18–20) Paul offers to pay for any financial damage caused by
            Onesimus's running away; *but* he implies that Philemon owes
            him something too. What is it? Do you think Philemon
            would seek to collect his losses from Paul?

The Conclusion

(v. 21)   What *might* Philemon have thought Paul meant by "doing
            more"? What more could he do?

(v. 22)   What probable effect would Paul's return have on Philemon?

(vv. 23–25) Note that Paul refers to all those listed as his fellow workers,
            the same term he applied to Philemon earlier. By mentioning
            these names, Paul suggests a mutual interest which binds
            Onesimus and himself together.

The benediction is for all the church (the *your* is plural).

128

So far, we've looked at what Paul was saying to his original audience, Philemon, about a specific subject: treatment of the slave Onesimus. Obviously we're living in totally different times: we don't own slaves today. So then what's the value of Paul's letter for us? Is there anything at all we can learn from it?

C. Worship

For worship today, read in unison the following question and answer from the Heidelberg Catechism, expressing how God has freed us by making us into servants:

Q. Why do you call him "Our Lord"?
A. Because—
    not with gold or silver,
    but with his precious blood—
  he has set us free
    from sin and from the tyranny of the devil,
  and has bought us,
    body and soul,
  to be his very own.

For Next Time: "God's Kind of Religion," chapter 25 in *Promises*, looks at the letters of Peter, James, and John. Read this chapter for next time.

It would also be helpful to read the (short) letter of 1 Peter, since next week in class you'll be asked to apply our six "How to Study the Bible" questions to that book. Please read 1 Peter at home this week, if at all possible.

God's Kind of Religion

A. Chapter Review

1. As Dr. Nederhood points out, some letters are disturbing. The letters of John, James, and Peter are like that. These letters tell us it's not enough to simply *say* we believe in Christ. To be "religious" means to "be actively involved with other people."

   —What did that mean for John?

   —What did that mean for James?

   —What did that mean for Peter?

2. Dr. Nederhood mentions several things we must *do* because we are saved. Mention a couple of them. Can you add anything to that list?

B. Bible Study

Read 1 Peter 2:9–10. Then, working alone, please write out answers to the "How to Study the Bible" questions on the following page. A few suggestions are given with each question.

131

1. *What is the literary style of this book?* List at least two things you might expect because of the kind of literature 1 Peter is.

2. *To what audience is the original message addressed?* Read 1 Peter 1:1–2, 6, 14, 17; 2:10, 19, 21; 3:15–16; 4:12–13; 5:10. Describe Peter's audience as fully as you can.

3. *Who is the author and what is the author's purpose in writing?* Check 5:13 for an additional fact or two about Peter. Considering Peter's audience, what do you suppose was his main purpose in writing? See also 1 Peter 1:6–7, 14; 2:2, 9; 4:13–14; 5:10, 12.

4. *What is the context of this passage (1 Pet. 2:9–10)?* What immediately precedes and follows the passage?

5. *What is the meaning of the key word(s) in this passage?* Look up two cross-references listed for our passage (1 Pet. 2:9–10). Then pick out just one phrase which seems to be the most important in our text. Finally, explain in a sentence or two what this phrase meant to Peter's original audience.

6. *What does this passage say about the covenant (partnership) between God and his people?* Answer this question first for Peter's original audience, then for Christians today.

C. Worship

The book of 1 Peter offers encouragement to those who suffer for Christ's sake. All of us in God's "holy nation" will face valleys in our faith, especially the "valley of the shadow of death." For worship today, think of a Scripture passage that gives you comfort on "down days." Read or summarize it for the class.

For Next Time: Theopneustos. That word is almost impossible to pronounce. However, Dr. Nederhood claims the meaning of that word lies at the heart of the Bible. He explains in chapter 26 of *Promises.* Read it for next time, and complete section A, as assigned.

Theopneustos

A. Chapter Review

1. Personal comments/questions on chapter 26:

2. Do you agree that the Bible is a special and unique book? If so, what do you think makes it so?

3. According to Dr. Nederhood, what accounts for the uniqueness of the Bible? What does 2 Timothy 3:16 mean by stating that all Scripture is *theopneustos*?

4. "I believe," says Dr. Nederhood, "that one must make a choice, a faith choice, either for or against the Bible." If I am "for" the Bible, what must I confess about it? What dangers must I avoid?

B. Bible Study

All scripture is inspired by God.... (RSV)
All scripture is God-breathed.... (NIV)

1. One method of understanding what the Bible means by *theopneustos* ("inspired" or "God-breathed") is to read other passages that refer to this idea. Some of these passages are listed below. Please read the passages and write, in your own words, what they say about the "breath of God."

   a. Genesis 2:7; Job 33:4; Psalm 33:6

   b. Ezekiel 2:1–2; 11:5

   c. John 20:22

   d. John 14:26; 16:13

   e. 2 Peter 1:20–21

2. A good question to ask is "So the Bible is inspired. What does that mean?" Second Timothy 3:16 answers that question. Try rewriting the section of the verse which follows the statement "All scripture is inspired by God..." in your own words. Using other versions or paraphrases may be helpful.

All scripture is inspired by God, _____

_____

_____

_____

_____

_____

_____

_____ .

3. According to verse 17, what is the end result of the Bible's being "inspired by God"?

4. To what extent do we actually use Scripture for the things mentioned in verse 16? Do you have any suggestions for having more and better times for personal Bible reading?

C. Worship

A prayer-litany from Psalm 119:33–40, NIV:

Leader: Teach me, O Lord, to follow your decrees;
then I will keep them to the end.

Group: Give me understanding, and I will keep your law
and obey it with all my heart.

Leader: Direct me in the path of your commands,
for there I find delight.

Group: Turn my heart toward your statutes
and not toward selfish gain.

Leader: Turn my eyes away from worthless things;
renew my life according to your word.

Group: Fulfill your promise to your servant,
so that you may be feared.

Leader: Take away the disgrace I dread,
for your laws are good.

All: How I long for your precepts!
Renew my life in your righteousness.
Amen

For Next Time: Read "The Point of No Return" (chapter 27) and complete section A, as assigned.

The Point of No Return

A. Chapter Review

1. Personal comments/questions on chapter 27:

2. Once past the point of no return, a person can't turn back—it would be disastrous. Chapter 27 says there's a point like that in the Christian faith. What is that point?

3. The immediate audience for the book of Hebrews was Jewish Christians who wanted to return to the ways and rituals of the Old Testament Jewish religion. Dr. Nederhood says Hebrews gives three ways of correcting "the human tendency to idolize the past." List those ways.

4. What's the "great message" of the book of Hebrews?

B. Bible Study

According to Hebrews, the Bible affects our lives whether we believe in God or not. If we are unbelieving, says Hebrews, God's Word is "sharper than any two-edged sword," exposing all our faults, all our cover-ups. But Hebrews assures us that if we are believers, God's Word is full of hope, because it pictures Jesus as the center of the Scriptures, as the only real light in a dark world.

Hebrews 4:14–16 portrays Jesus as a high priest who has *sympathy* for his people. That's the key word—sympathy. The context of verses 14–16 reveals the unknown author of Hebrews urging his Jewish audience—some of whom had slipped away from Christianity—to remain faithful to Jesus, to "strive" to enter his eternal rest.

Today's Bible study concentrates mostly on what these verses meant to the original audience and what they mean to us today.

Verse 14

1. Jesus here is called a "great high priest." What was the task of the Old Testament high priests? (See Hebrews 5:1.)

2. To the Jewish audience of Hebrews, this verse brought images of a priest who, on the Day of Atonement, would slowly pass from the outer tabernacle into the sacred Holy of Holies. By way of contrast, what has Christ done? How does this make him a "great" high priest?

3. What did "let us hold fast our confession" probably mean to the audience of Hebrews?

Verse 15

1. Look up the word *sympathy*. What does it mean that Christ is able to "sympathize with our weaknesses"?

2. How can the phrase "yet without sinning" comfort us?

3. Some conservative Christians also think of Jesus as removed from us and all our smallness, dirt, and panic. These Christians think Jesus Christ is alive. But they think he is not, and has never been, really human. He is lofty, misty, high, and lifted up. He never laughed. He never dropped a tool or bent a nail. Even as a boy, his knuckles were always clean.... "The little Lord Jesus, no crying he makes." He is unreal! He is remote.
but...
To many people Jesus is a familiar figure. His picture hangs in the kitchen. His name is a household word. Songs about him—some of them sweet, intimate, sentimental—are played all day as a broadcast background to household tasks. Jesus is a "dear, familiar friend."
From Beyond Doubt by Cornelius Plantinga.
Copyright 1980 by the Board of Publications of the Christian Reformed Church.

What's wrong with these views of Christ?

If Christ ought to be neither remote nor overly familiar, how should we see him?

Verse 16

1. What word ties this verse to the previous two verses?

2. What can we *do* if we take this verse seriously?

C. Worship

For worship today, pray to God silently, asking him to give mercy and grace for someone else's needs, as well as for your own. Before you begin, then, think of one personal need you have and a need you know someone else has. Now, together, pray silently and specifically that Jesus will sympathize with those needs.

For Next Time: Some people think life is absurd; it's a joke, it makes no sense. Not true! says Dr. Nederhood, in the last chapter of *Promises.* The book of Revelation says life is serious. Read "From Silence to Sound" for next time.

From Silence to Sound

A. Chapter Review

For this last chapter of *Promises*, please be ready to tell the class what you personally found most interesting, encouraging, or challenging about the chapter and/or your reading from Revelation. Jot some notes below, if you wish.

B. Bible Study

Revelation's Author/Purpose/Audience

Revelation (often called the *apocalypse*, meaning "uncovering") was written by the apostle John from the Isle of Patmos, where he had been exiled because of his testimony for Christ. The book was probably written between A.D. 81–98. It is addressed to the seven churches of Asia, which were undergoing persecution for the sake of the gospel. Its purpose was to comfort and encourage these churches in their struggle against the demonic elements loose in the world, assuring these churches of their participation in Christ's ultimate victory over evil.

Revelation is a record—in symbolic language or word pictures—of John's vision describing the events that would lead to the final establishment of God's eternal kingdom. As a vision, Revelation must not be interpreted with historical literalism (relating its symbols to specific events at *any* point in history or in the future).

The Context of Today's Passage for Study

The first three chapters of Revelation feature a word from the Son of Man to the seven churches. Chapters 4–5 give us John's second vision: a scene of God Almighty enthroned in heaven, and of the Lamb, who alone is worthy to take the scroll and to show the meaning of the hidden things of history. Chapter 6 describes the first seals being opened, revealing the wars, famines, and judgment that are part of the history of the world. Chapter 8 begins

143

with the opening of the seventh seal. After about one-half hour of silence in heaven, seven angels appear and blow seven trumpets. Natural wonders and disasters appear, and we see the punishment of those who reject the gospel. Finally, in chapter 11, the seventh trumpet gives a summary of all the trumpets and what they proclaim. Loud voices in heaven announce the conclusion.

Bible study

Read Revelation 11:15-19. Then answer our first—and most important—"How to Study the Bible" question: *What does this passage say about the covenant (partnership) between God and his people?* Please write your answer below:

C. Worship

After the vision of God's judgment and the multitudes praising King Jesus, John—inspired by God—pictures our final, full fellowship with God. Listen to the reading from Revelation 21 and 22 (RSV).

A transcript of the tape, segment 12, follows:

Then I saw a new heaven and a new earth; for the first heaven and the first earth had passed away, and the sea was no more. And I saw the holy city, new Jerusalem, coming down out of heaven from God, prepared as a bride adorned for her husband; and I heard a loud voice from the throne saying, "Behold, the dwelling of God is with men. He will dwell with them, and they shall be his people, and God himself will be with them; he will wipe away every tear from their eyes, and death shall be no more, neither shall there be mourning nor crying nor pain any more, for the former things have passed away."

And I saw no temple in the city, for its temple is the Lord God the Almighty and the Lamb. And the city has no need of sun or moon to shine upon it, for the glory of God is its light, and its lamp is the Lamb. By its light shall the nations walk; and the kings of the earth shall bring their glory into it, and its gates shall never be shut by day—and there shall be no night there; they shall bring into it the glory and the honor of the nations. But nothing unclean shall enter it, nor any one who practices abomination or falsehood, but only those who are written in the Lamb's book of life.

Then he showed me the river of the water of life, bright as crystal, flowing from the throne of God and of the Lamb through the middle of the street of the city; also, on either side of the river, the tree of life with its twelve kinds of fruit, yielding its fruit each month; and the leaves of the tree were for the healing of the nations. There shall no more be anything accursed, but the throne of God and of the Lamb shall be in it, and his servants shall worship him; they shall see his face, and his name shall be on their foreheads. And night shall be no more; they need no light of lamp or sun, for the Lord God will be their light, and they shall reign for ever and ever.

Personal Evaluation

At the end of this course, it may be helpful to evaluate what you've learned about God's Word. Here are a few questions to consider. Feel free to add your own questions as well.

1. To what extent did the course help me reach my goals? (See Introductory Session for statements of what the course was supposed to teach.)

2. What methods of studying the Bible were most helpful to me? Which of the "How to Study the Bible" questions do I expect to use in my future Bible study?

3. Did this survey course on the Bible give me a better understanding of the oneness of God's Word? If so, what did I learn about the single message of the Scriptures?

4. What part of this course meant the most to me in my personal faith?

5. What might I do (or do differently) as a result of taking this course?